Integral Animal Behavior

CURRENT CONCEPTS IN BIOLOGY

A Macmillan Series

NORMAN H. GILES WALTER KENWORTHY JOHN G. TORREY, Editors

Integral Animal Behavior

David E. Davis
The Pennsylvania State University

The Macmillan Company, New York
Collier-Macmillan Limited, London

First Printing

Library of Congress catalog card number: 66-16094

The Macmillan Company, New York

Collier-Macmillan Canada, Ltd., Toronto, Ontario

Printed in the United States of America

Preface

THE VIEWPOINT on biology adopted in this booklet is that behavior is an integrating mechanism which brings animals together in populations in contrast to mechanisms which bring cells together into organs or molecules into cells. Thus, the molecular viewpoint considers the rudiments of integration, since all living matter is composed of chemical substances. The processes proceed upward, both in the evolutionary and in the integrative scale, until one deals with whole organisms that in various ways have to get along with each other. Integration of animals into a population is brought about through physiological devices such as nerves and hormones. The activity of these devices is stimulated in part by external conditions such as temperature or light. However, an additional set of stimuli comes from other animals whose actions cause an individual to move about according to the needs of the particular situation.

This book will summarize the anatomical and physiological foundations for behavior, going on to a relatively brief consideration of the behavior of individual organisms. Some attention will be devoted to sexual behavior, since this feature is vital for maintenance of the species. The culmination of the book deals with the behavioral aspects of the integration of individuals into a coherent population which itself generates new types of population behavior. Thus, some species have attained a new level of organization in which the population itself is the unit and may even include members of other species.

The book, of course, does not intend to be exhaustive but will, I hope, stimulate the reader to a broad view of the sweep of changes in behavior from isolated organisms to populations. Suggestions for additional reading are given at the end of most chapters. These references have been chosen in part for their availability as well as for the quality of the material.

I am indebted to Dr. Martin W. Schein for careful reading of the manuscript.

D. E. D.

Contents

Integral Animal Behavior

CHAPTER 1

Introduction

WHAT DOES YOUR DOG do all day long? Watch him closely on a summer day when he spends most of his time out of doors. In the morning on a cool day he may, after waking up, wander around a bit, then settle down in the bright but early morning sun. He will remain resting for some time, then get up and do something else. He may hear a strange noise and run out barking to see what is happening; or he may simply, in a surge of activity, wander around the yard. Around noontime he may settle down under a bush or in some shady place where it is cool and take a rather long sleep. But in the afternoon, he will again respond to people and associate with the individuals that enter his realm. In the late afternoon he will normally become much more active and, if not fed at his usual time, will bark or jump at the door where his food is customarily placed. After feeding he generally lies down to rest in a place of appropriate temperature. Later he may be disturbed by some noise or some person and respond by barking and chasing. The behavior of the dog is a constant response to the environmental situation. When it is cool, the dog finds places where he can keep warm. When it is warm, he finds places where he can keep cool. The activities within his environment are a constant stimulus to him. He runs to meet people or other dogs, he barks at a truck that goes past, or at small boys on bicycles.

This response of a dog to his environmental situation ensures a constant adjustment to the habitat and, through this adjustment, the survival of the individual. A wide variety of organs are involved. Events within the environment of a dog are detected by the senses of smell, sound, sight, and by even more complicated receptors. These messages are transmitted through nerves to the appropriate organs, whether they be muscles, glands, or the digestive tract, and action is taken in accordance with the message.

Behavior may be defined as what an animal does. It accomplishes two major objectives. The first is the adjustment of the individual to the environmental circumstances. Such accommodations to changes in the environment, either within the day or within the year, are necessary for the survival of the individual. Naturally, during the year many far more complicated situations arise than occur in a simple day of a domestic dog. There are such elaborate behavioral processes as the migration of birds, the hibernation of rodents, the winter dormancy of insects, and the dormant stages and multiplication phases of invertebrates, to mention only a few. These adjustments serve to maintain the individual. The second objective is another set of adjustments that serve to preserve the species by means of reproduction. Basically, this second type of adjustment functions in essentially the same manner—namely, reception of the stimuli through the sense organs which send messages through nerves or through hormones to other organs which act upon receipt of the information. However, the survival of a species is maintained by the production of young, a process that immediately adds a social aspect. In part, this sociality is required by those forms that reproduce sexually and in part by the evolutionary tendency for the young to be cared for over longer and longer periods of development by the adults. In the most primitive forms the egg and sperm meet in the water quite by chance, and the development of the young is completely independent of the adults. However, the adjustment to the environment by the young is favored by the assistance of the adults, and the meeting of male and female is favored by a variety of behavior patterns. Thus, there is evolutionary pressure toward sociality and behaviors that adjust one individual to another.

Lastly, it must be recognized that behavior is constantly evolving by means of adjustment to the environment, whether it be to the physical aspects or to other individuals. There are pressures for more successful adjustment which, of course, means more successful survival. Under these circumstances, it is no surprise that innumerable types of adjustment occur and that long chains of evolutionary sequence can be illustrated in behavior as well as in anatomy. An example that illustrates the interlocking of behavior, physiology, and anatomy is the evolution of viviparity in snakes. The ability to hold the young in the body for part of its development has originated in many species presumably as a result of survival advantages. Some of these are behavioral, such as protection from predators and from cold situations. A viviparous snake can keep the eggs at more favorable temperatures by moving about.

An attribute of behavior that permeates other fields of biology is the reduction of genetic variability permitted by learning and experience. An animal does not need to have a "gene" for every situation or contingency. To do this would require an impossible number of molecular combinations and result in rigidity. However, animals can learn how to behave under various circumstances and thus get along with a limited (but large) number of genes. Indeed, many of these genes concern the organization of the animal so that it can learn. Evolution has included a relative increase in the information derived from experience (learning) in contrast to the information derived from the genetic code. Man, of course, has relegated the genetic part of behavior to a minor role.

The scope of this volume is restricted for the most part to a consideration of the whole animal. The animal reacts as an integrated unit to features in its habitat. The parts of the animal have different functions that must be coordinated to produce appropriate action in response to the conditions of the habitat. The pressure of evolution has been toward the control by the animal of the habitat. The very primitive forms were completely at the mercy of the environmental exigencies, whereas the most highly developed vertebrates, in some cases, control the habitat except for extreme catastrophes. The central theme here is what an animal does in adjusting to its habitat conditions. Clearly, this emphasis depends on some knowledge of auxiliary features of biology. For example, what an animal does and how it does it clearly are related to its anatomical equipment, so a knowledge of anatomy is essential to the understanding of behavior. Similarly, the ability of an animal to translate by its sense organs a message into activity depends on the function, or physiology, of the various parts of its body; thus one must have some knowledge of physiology. Furthermore, how an animal behaves depends upon its past experiences and requires some understanding of many aspects, especially the learning part, of psychology. And lastly, of course, one cannot discuss response to the environment without knowing the ecological circumstances in which the animal lives. Thus this viewpoint on behavior integrates at least four major areas—anatomy, physiology, psychology, and ecology—into the whole animal in an attempt to understand what it does and how its relations to the habitat have evolved.

The plan of the book is first to discuss, in a rather brief manner, the equipment available to animals for carrying out adjustment to their habitat. Then several chapters deal, in an evolutionary treatment, with the means of adjusting and how it has developed within the animal kingdom. The treatment is not intended to be exhaustive but primarily to expose the reader to concepts rather than to a flood of facts. Examples are used sparingly but are intended to help the reader remember the concept rather than to burden him with details. In an attempt to make the examples more interesting, they are chosen almost entirely from recent original papers rather than from textbooks or review articles. However, in some cases, as in the preceding description of the dog, it is expected that the reader will already have an example in mind from his everyday experience. The approach also is intended to stimulate the reader to thinking and exploring the field of animal behavior. Therefore, there is no hesitation in noting unsolved problems and in posing questions which are food for thought or a source of possibilities for experimentation and research. Finally, it is hoped the reader will be stimulated to think more deeply and to carry out at least modest experimentation on his own at future times.

Behavior of Plants

In considering problems of integral behavior there is justification for restricting the discussion to animals. However, plants have the same basic protoplasmic composition and need to solve the same problems. Although primitive plants started out in the same way as did animals, their evolution has emphasized different methods. The unicellular organisms, classified as plants because they produce their own energy by means of chlorophyll or some other pigment, respond in essentially the same manner as do unicellular animals. They are in many cases responsive to light or dark, and they react to chemicals in their environment. Generally speaking, they do not have elaborate organelles for receiving stimuli from the environment but simply respond as a whole cell.

The higher plants also respond to many stimuli but in terms of the part rather than the whole. Thus parts of many plants turn in relation to the direction of light. The sunflower is the classic example. Another type of response is to pressure (touch). Leaves of many plants, mimosa for example, will bend away when touched by some object. An elaboration of this process is found in the pitcher plant which captures insects simply by enfolding them in a leaf. Many plants have seeds that in one way or another bend or even jump when touched. The familiar touch-me-not that grows in moist places has a device to make the seeds jump a distance of several feet when the seed capsule is touched. Another manner of behavior is the response by cells to increased or decreased turgor, produced by expelling or absorbing water in such a manner that the leaf or stem bends in response to stimuli.

Obviously, the behavior of plants has by no means attained the complexity of the behavior of animals. The important distinction, of course, is that plants lack the means of fast communication (nerves) developed by animals. Plants have hormones and use them for communication of information to other parts of a plant. However, hormones, although integrative, act slowly. Without a rapid and effective means of communication plants are limited to simple behavior patterns. However, it needs to be recognized that the basic reason for behavior is to solve problems of existence. Plants (as well as some animals) clearly have solved these problems by development of fantastically high reproductive rates. The number of seeds and spores produced by plants are so high that the mortality of the early stages can be and is astronomical. Coupled with this high production of progeny are many highly effective means of dispersal. Ocean and air currents, as well as traveling animals, have been used for spreading seeds far and wide, often in highly protected dormant stages which may remain viable for decades. Under these circumstances, for the species to survive movement is unnecessary; if a location is unfavorable, no matter—other individuals will get to favorable locations. In simple terms a plant waits for its energy to come to it; an animal goes to get it. Thus plants, without more than the rudiments of behavior, have successfully solved the problems of existence.

CHAPTER

2

Behavioral Equipment

THE FIRST PROBLEM ENCOUNTERED by an animal in its adjustment to the environment is recognition of the things present in the habitat. Animals have taken advantage of a number of physical stimuli from the environment to identify external conditions or objects: the pull of gravity, heat or cold from the surrounding medium, various chemicals in the medium, and rays of energy. Although animals might have used other stimuli, such as radio waves, to learn more about the environment, they have not. The environment contains many aspects that are not sensed by animals and hence not relevant to their existence. Man, on the other hand, has developed a technology to pick up environmental cues, such as radio waves, and translate them into a physical system (audible waves) that can be sensed by humans. This process is strictly analogous to the use of wavelengths of light from the environment. Some kind of electrical apparatus picks up waves and translates them into sound waves having a frequency audible to humans or into light waves of a frequency visible to humans. The invention of nonbiological devices for picking up cues from the environment is an original contribution of humans.

Animals have invented a variety of biological devices to pick up cues from the environment and to translate them into electrical (nervous) impulses. However, many environmental aspects are not detected by animals, and thus serve no useful purpose. Other aspects may actually be harmful even though not detected by the animals. For example, consider x-rays, which normally do not occur in nature but are harmful. Animals lack direct receptors for x-rays to warn them of danger, although recent research suggests some perception. Hence, under the artificial circumstances in the production of x-rays, animals are harmed. Presumably, were x-rays a regular feature of the environment, only those species that had developed some device to warn of x-rays would have survived.

Animals have learned through experience that only a few kinds of stimuli have meaning. Consider the dog which, of course, will respond to noises in its environment. If boys on bicycles make noise, the dog may rush out and bark at them. However, if an airplane goes overhead making a hundred times as much noise, the dog will scarcely look up. Thus, the boys on the bicycles have a meaning to the dog but the airplane has none, and the actual magnitude of the physical stimulus of sound has little importance for the dog. The environment consists of things that give cues meaningful to particular needs of the animal. For example, the world around a dog is entirely different from the world around a human, a bee, or a protozoan. While the environment around a dog emphasizes smells and objects on the ground, that around a bee includes primarily different wavelengths of light and their planes of polarization. The protozoan's environment, however, is a set of chemical and physical stimuli emphasizing inorganic ions and diffused light.

An obvious corollary to the proposition that animals respond to certain stimuli relevant to the species is the proposition that animals ignore irrelevant stimuli and fail to discriminate among objects not regularly encountered. A dog may ignore thunder but respond to the squeal of a mouse. Gulls will roll eggs into their nest from a distance of a few inches but not from a foot or more; in normal life a gull might kick an egg a few inches off the edge of the nest but not a foot or more. An object a foot away could not be an "egg."

Internal Environment

In addition to senses for the external environment, animals have primitive responses to the internal environment. The cells that compose organs maintain sensitivity to a variety of physical factors and respond, in many respects, the same as a one-celled protozoan. Indeed, individual cells respond to a variety of stimuli whether they are acting as an entire animal or as part of an animal. For example, the lowly amoeba is generally sensitive to light and to a number of chemical stimuli. In higher animals irritability of cells is maintained and in some cases kept as a generalized activity. The sturgeon has cells in the epidermis that do not respond to special cues but simply react to stimuli of many types. These cells seem to be a generalized system useful to the sturgeon in indicating the environmental conditions. Cells within organs have maintained this responsiveness and in some cases have specialized to particular stimuli. Vertebrates have a respiratory center in the brain where cells are especially responsive to changes in the carbon dioxide content of the blood. This respiratory center controls, through nerves, the breathing of the individual and can be considered a sense organ just as the eye, which responds to an external condition and initiates behavioral action. Groups of similar cells with special responsiveness for conditions external to the cell occur in the hunger and thirst centers of the brain. We note, thus, that there is no fundamental difference between responsive cells that detect conditions within a body and responsive cells that detect external environmental situations.

Multicellular animals have two levels of organization: in one the cells act within an organ to control the organ's behavior; and in the other the organs act within the whole organism to alter the organism's behavior. A third behavioral level (animals within a population) is possible and may be in the process of development, at least in certain species. A sense for detecting the external conditions of an entire population is useful. For example, the temperature of a hive of bees is maintained almost constant during the year by actions of the entire colony that maintain heat in winter and coolness in summer. A type of sense organ acting for the whole colony may be evolving. Similarly, among vertebrates the density of the population is vitally important for a species' survival, and a sense of density may be evolving at the present time.

Learning

The role of learning in decisions made by an animal in response to stimuli from the environment is vitally important. Without becoming involved in a discussion of the different types of learning or the laws of learning, it can be said simply that an individual through his experience associates certain cues with harmful, and others with beneficial, situations. Through differential survival this learning is incorporated into the hereditary mechanisms so that individuals have innate responses to particular stimuli. Very primitive types of behavior, which are apparently analogous to learning, occur among invertebrates and even protozoa. However, an amoeba is unable to attach real meaning to cues that would warn it of danger. When placed in an environment near some noxious substance it will, upon receiving stimuli, move away from the dangerous chemical but may by random movements return again and again to the substance. Those individuals that come too close to the chemical are destroyed.

Learning influences behavior of the individual and increases its flexibility. However, even in mammals the responses are a mixture of innate behavior patterns and learning. Consider the behavior of a dog toward foods. He has an innate appetite for meat and certain other foods, such as fruits. Among these he will learn that certain ones taste good and others do not. For example, a dog will eat a pheasant with relish but discard a starling after a few sniffs. He has learned that for some reason starlings are distasteful. However, he never has an interest in lettuce or carrots unless, of course, they are thoroughly mixed with some meat. He never bothers to learn that some vegetables are good eating. In contrast, a rabbit has an innate disposition to eat vegetables and never bothers to learn that certain kinds of meat are palatable. Thus, an animal responds to the sensory cues from the environment in a manner dictated in part by a hereditary disposition and in part by learning, which has occurred during the animal's lifetime. Learning may be used to overcome disadvantageous situations. For example, certain small fish live within the sea anemone, which has tentacles armed with poison darts (nematocysts). Normally the anemone kills and digests an animal that enters, but certain fish have learned to avoid the tentacles generally and to profit from protection by the anemone.

Senses

The senses, of course, primitively detect only the conditions of the environment. A paramecium detects an acid in its environment and moves away from it. However, the protozoan does not know what to do, except to get out. An advance in response to the environment is to develop organs for detection of danger that indicate what action to take. Usually one sense modality detects the danger, and another determines the possible action. For example, a bird hears the call of a hawk, but it sees the shelter to which it can immediately fly. Clearly, the bird has a greater chance of survival when it knows what to do about danger in a detailed manner than if it merely knew that it had to get out of the particular location. Perhaps an example will show that this principle applies to humans as well. Consider a situation in which a passenger tells the driver of an automobile, "Look out!" This warning says nothing about what the danger is or what might be done about it. The driver simply knows that danger is somewhere. If, however, the passenger says,

"A truck is coming, turn right," the driver has an immediate course of action and an improved chance of survival.

When an animal receives information from the exterior, it must, of course, do something about it. In primitive, one-celled animals transmission of information to the active part of the cell is no problem. But in more complex animals some system must be devised to transmit information to a central coordinating area which sends messages to the appropriate muscles or organs for action. Two types of connections exist. The first, the nervous system, is designed primarily for rapid communication of information about a temporary situation. The brain or other central organ in various animals may be slightly or elaborately developed for sorting out the messages coming from the exterior and sending them through the proper nerves to muscles that can act. In this way the animal promptly reacts to the environment.

Hormones, another type of connection, have developed in many forms, especially in insects and vertebrates. Actually, some hormones have arisen as a specialization of chemicals given off by nerves. Hormones generally act slowly, since they are produced in quantity by some special organ which takes considerable time to increase its production. There are many advantages in a system of communication that, so to speak, averages information about conditions in the environment in contrast to reactions that are too prompt and reflect only a very temporary situation. Studies of the breeding behavior of birds show that in many species the proper hormonal condition is necessary for a male and a female to enter into copulation. Given the proper hormonal conditions, the particular behavior of a female will stimulate the male to copulate. Now in the absence of the hormones, a particular behavioral stimulus, such as a posture of the female, might cause the male to copulate at any time of year or under any circumstances. If this attempt occurred in the fall or in the winter, there would be no real survival value, although perhaps no harm would result. It is advantageous to the species to concentrate their copulatory behavior in the particular season when habitat conditions are conducive to nesting and survival of the young. The proper season, of course, is the time of abundant vegetation which, speaking generally, occurs after rainfalls. Now let us consider some species that respond to sudden rains by an increase in the reproductive hormones and so eventually breed. A brief shower which might stimulate the nervous system has little effect because only a prolonged period of rain will start the functioning of the hormone system. However, even this relationship seems to be too risky, and most temperate species have added an additional safety factor to prevent breeding in response to a very temporary situation. Many birds have developed a response to an increasing length of day. Generally speaking, an increasing length of day occurs at the season when, following a rise in temperature and adequate rainfall, the vegetation and hence the food supply becomes available. The regularly increasing length of day averages, in terms of stimulus, the seasons for literally centuries, and many species have developed a response to the slowly increasing length of day in such a manner that, for the most part, the animals begin reproduction at a time when the food and shelter are suitable. Thus a system of communication that averages conditions over a period of time has a vitally important role in indicating to an animal what the environmental conditions are. Hormones serve this averaging function.

Organs

The sense organs are generally collections of specialized cells, although, as mentioned, some animals have rather generalized cells throughout the body which respond to external cues. The advantage of specialization of cells into particular organs lies in the identification of the particular kind of dangerous or favorable situation. Without this specialization the only information the animal would

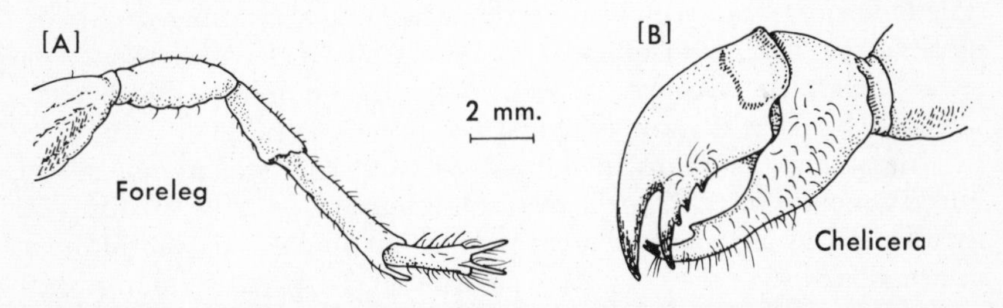

Figure 2·1. Sense organs of the scorpion. A: Tactile hairs on legs. B: Chemoreceptors on chelicera. These, and other receptors, provide the scorpion with information about its environment. [From F. T. Abushama, in *Animal Behaviour*, 12 (1), 1964.]

obtain from sense organs would be a rather generalized statement that something is in the environment. The sense organs are, of course, located where they are useful (Figure 2·1). In most cases, the head accumulates sense organs, since the animal is moving head first. However, a number of invertebrates have organs located on the posterior part of the body, and a mammal, the mole, has tactile hairs on its tail which help it to run through a tunnel backward as rapidly as forward.

Animals use various anatomical and physical structures to detect conditions in the environment. One could classify organs in a number of ways, and one logical classification is according to the type of physical stimulus.

GRAVITY. The most primitive and simplest stimulus seems to be gravity. This information tells an animal what his position is and whether he is in the proper relationship to the earth. It should be noted that another force, magnetism, has not been used by animals, as far as we know, although some chitons accumulate iron in the radula which is polarized. A possible reason is the inability of animals to find little pieces of iron to use in detecting magnetic direction. In contrast, gravity can be sensed by the device of little stones of various sorts in an organ that permit detection of the direction of pull.

TEMPERATURE. Sense organs respond to another type of physical stimulus called relative temperature—that is, heat or cold. Animals do not measure temperature in physical terms of degrees but have cells that respond to a relatively hot or cold object. However, even for heat and cold the animals have responses limited to meaningful levels in terms of their lives. For example, mites have heat receptors on head or palps that respond to levels of temperature in the range of the body heat of birds or mammals. But mites have no response for very high temperatures; they never (normally) encounter them. While usually heat or cold is merely a means of assessing the favorableness of the environment, it may in some cases be useful for other meanings. Locusts, for example, march more (cover more area) at high temperatures than at low.

CHEMICALS. Organs also react to chemicals which may affect membrane permeability or by their concentration alter diffusion gradients. A paramecium responds to such chemical substances. Since chemical substances are so widespread in the environment and so diversified, it is no surprise that these stimuli are frequently put to work as taste or smell. Their diversity means that animals can attach definite meaning to a particular substance. The male giraffe, for example, literally tastes the urine of a female to determine whether she is in heat; the chemical (as yet not identified) has a very specific meaning. Among ants the worker that discovers a food supply lays a chemical train which guides other workers to the location.

ENERGY. Another physical character used by animals is energy in the form of waves that include visible light. Although a wide spectrum of frequencies is available, animals use only a very small fraction. Some use waves called visible light; others pick up waves beyond this range. We are familiar with the rays in the visible part of the spectrum. The differences in wavelengths provide opportunity for such refinements as color vision, permitting an animal to detect more details. Each species has a capacity to respond to particular wavelengths, although animals within a group such as birds respond to similar lengths. Insects, in contrast, respond to rather different lengths, especially to the ultraviolet. Recently it has been demonstrated that many invertebrates use polarization of light as a cue. Bees in particular use the property of polarized light from the sun for orientation. A crab (*Ocypode*) orients to its burrow and another (*Goniopsis*) orients itself perpendicular to the water's edge by polarization of light. Some species of cephalopods also orient in the water according to polarized light.

PRESSURE. Another physical force that has been utilized is pressure produced either by air waves or by direct contact. This attribute gives animals an additional opportunity to respond, by means of waves in a medium, to stimuli at a distance. It is usually called hearing and occurs only in the highest invertebrates and vertebrates. However, the basic physical attribute is pressure on cells, which results in slight deformation and a consequent response. The elementary type of pressure results from contact with either an external object or some internal structure. Thus, as I write, I feel the pressure of the desk on my arm and hence know where my arm is. Innumerable objects can exert pressure directly, but animals have developed a neat device to use pressure of air or water (waves of particular lengths) to get information about environment at a distance through hearing organs.

ELECTRICITY. Another physical phenomenon, electricity, has been used by a few animals. Recent studies show that some aquatic species produce an electrical field as they swim. The prime function seems to be communication to other members of the species. In a few species the electrical impulse is very strong and is used either for killing prey or for protection. The electric shock produced by an eel can kill a horse. In this case, an organ that apparently first served for communication evolved into one for protection.

Six physical forces or attributes—gravity, temperature, chemicals, energy (waves), pressure, and electricity—have been appropriated by animals to detect the environmental conditions. However, not all physical attributes have been used, as previously mentioned. Magnetic forces are not known to be used, although crabs whose equilibrium stones have been replaced by iron filings react to magnetic forces. Even within one type of physical attribute, not all parts are used; only a few wavelengths of energy have been appropriated.

Research, however, is active in these topics and perhaps we will discover that some animals use cosmic rays or gamma radiation, possibly for seasonal or daily rhythms.

Before discussing the particular sense modalities in some detail it is desirable to mention that animals have developed long-range and short-range systems for detection of environmental conditions. It is clearly advantageous for an animal to detect danger at a distance, thereby giving more time and opportunity to react to the situation. Long-range and short-range systems have developed for several types of physical stimulus. Long-range detection is provided by the sense of smell, which is basically a chemical feature. Other long-range sense modalities are sight and hearing, which rely on energy reactions and pressure for their activation. Through these three senses an animal may learn about conditions at a distance as well as about conditions nearby. Short-range conditions are detected primarily by chemical sense such as taste and mechanical sense such as pressure. Temperature and pressure on internal organs also indicate conditions adjacent to the animal.

While animals have developed the ability to respond to near or far stimuli, an additional development is the production of behaviors that differ according to whether the stimulus is near or far. For example, certain animals have vocalizations that are used for notification either at a distance or close by. The starling has two advertising calls whose basic function is to notify another individual that the bird owns a particular nest hole. When a starling sees a flying starling at a distance, it gives a very loud call that ascends and descends in pitch. This note proclaims at a distance of hundreds of yards that the nest hole is owned by the bird. Then if the stranger comes close, the starling uses a different call, which again indicates the same idea but is used for close-range information. The animal thus has a double assurance of effectiveness of communication.

Information

The preceding paragraphs have discussed sense organs from the viewpoint of the physical stimuli that are received. It now is desirable to discuss the kind of environmental information obtained through the sense organs.

Position. Animals, of course, need to know whether they are in the proper position in relation to their environment, in a medium such as air or water or on the floor of the ocean or the ground. For this function gravity is generally the physical characteristic utilized. Many animals have developed anatomical organs that consist of some small stones located in such a way that they press upon nerve endings. The organ of crabs and other invertebrates is usually called the statocyst. For the vertebrates the utriculus performs the same functions. Generally the nervous components simply tell the animal whether it is upright or not. However, among crabs there are two types of sensory hairs attached to different sets of nerves. One indicates the position of the animal; the other indicates movement. Thus, the animal not only can tell whether it is upright but also whether it is moving. Among the vertebrates the labyrinth organs indicate the extent of tilting of the head which, of course, is an indicator of the bodily position. Statoliths or other similar organs differ greatly from phylum to phylum in their anatomical conditions, and they are widely prevalent because the position sense is so basic to an animal's orientation. It must be noted that while gravity is the basic physical characteristic used to determine position, the information on position is translated through pressure on nerves. Another physical characteristic, light, is also used to determine position. However, such use occurs only after the animal has learned by experience about the environmental conditions.

A second aspect an animal must consider in relation to its position is the location of its legs or other extremities. If an animal did not have some means of knowing where its legs were, it would have considerable difficulty in initiating behavior. Serving this function are nerve endings called proprioceptors that respond to a mechanical stimulus produced by stretching. Through these nerves crabs, for example, can know where their legs are and can move their legs in any particular direction without having to look at them. Phalangids (daddy longlegs) have special sensory cells in slits in the legs which are proprioceptive and indicate where each leg is—a rather necessary piece of information when so many legs are involved! This sense is so basic and so regularly taken for granted that it is often neglected. Consider how difficult life would be if one did know the location of his arm.

Environmental Conditions. The sense of temperature (detection of heat or cold) is usually relatively simple and is rare among the invertebrates. The reason, of course, that it is not common is that most invertebrates live in an aqueous medium in a very constant temperature, so the animals rarely need information about this external condition. Even if they had information, they could do little about it. However, a number of other forms, especially the vertebrates, have cells on the surface of the body to indicate hot or cold conditions. Among the mammals there are two sets: one indicates conditions that are hot; the other indicates conditions that are cold.

In sharks, however, special cells are located in groups on the head. A change in the temperature of the water results in nerve impulses that are inverse in their frequency to the change in temperature. Thus, when the shark enters a cool area, nerve impulses increase in frequency, but when the shark goes to the warm area, the impulses decrease in frequency.

One additional sense modality, pressure, indicates the general conditions surrounding the animal. Pressure is important for species living in an aquatic environment, especially in the oceans. The primitive invertebrates such as ctenophores, hydromedusae, polychaetes, and larvae of decapods are greatly influenced by pressure and have cells that indicate the local conditions. Generally, the animal is able by swimming to get to a favorable area. The aquatic vertebrates, fish, have developed a lateral line organ which indicates the general conditions of pressure so the animal can adjust to changing conditions. These organs are mechanoreceptors located in the skin sometimes with rather elaborate protective structures. The organs often develop about the head and permit a fish to "feel" at a distance of several centimeters, thereby detecting moving animals at short distances. The organ consists of neuromasts which are clusters of pear-shaped sensory cells having hairs that project into a jelly-like substance.

The chemical sense, including taste and smell, serves first to indicate in a general way the conditions of the environment such as salinity but more particularly to indicate specific objects within the environment useful to the animal. Thus, the chemical sense has evolved additional functions in providing information. In general, taste and smell have separate anatomical structures. While taste is a means of getting information from objects in immediate contact with the animal, smell is useful for detection of objects at a distance. The chemical sense is extremely widespread; it occurs in snails, earthworms, crabs, and almost all vertebrates. However, one group of vertebrates, birds, have almost completely lost the sense of smell (except vultures) and have only a poorly developed sense of taste. The chemical sense is, of course, the utilization of a general cellular reaction which occurs in protozoa, sponges, and others. Indeed, one can consider that sperm have a chemical sense, since they are attracted to the substances given off by ova in a number of situations. Rabbit sperm attach to rabbit ova but not to rat ova. Thus, one can refer to the behavior of sperm as well as to the behavior of a complete animal. This idea can be extended to cells within the body. Some blood cells, leukocytes, are attracted to chemotactic substances given off by bacteria.

The multiplicity of chemicals in the environment, of course, permits animals to attach individual meaning to chemicals from a variety of different things, different food substances, and different predators. A mollusc (*Monacuta*) that lives commensally with an echinoderm is attracted by a chemical stimulus from the host. A polychaete worm is attracted to its host, a pinnotherid crab, by proteins. Larvae of barnacles will settle only on surfaces that already have certain proteins from barnacles.

Often the chemicals are detected by cells grouped together into an organ. Molluscs, for example, have osphradia at the opening of the mantle cavity, where the water currents can bring chemicals in direct contact with many cells. As is well known, vertebrates have taste buds and special cells for the detection of smell. The chemical sense, because it can respond to so many particular substances, has allowed the development of complexity. The first phase, the simple detection of habitat conditions, soon became elaborated into the provision of information about particular types of foods. Then the further development of use of chemicals in mating behavior was added. To illustrate, in sea slugs certain chemicals stimulate copulatory behavior. In ascidians, ciliated pits sample the water entering the mouth, and when stimuli from sperm enter these pits, gonadotrophic hormones are released, which in turn release the ova. Many examples occur among insects. The male drosophila releases a chemical which, when received by the antennae of the female, stimulates the mating behavior. Longhorn beetles perform an elaborate mating ceremony including frequent licking of antennae. The use of the chemical sense in mating behavior of vertebrates requires no elaboration. A recent discovery shows that male mice produce a chemical serving to stimulate females to come into heat. Removal of olfactory bulbs from sows results in failure to come into heat, presumably from lack of stimulation.

The reception of light provides additional information about the environment. The universality of rays of energy has naturally permitted utilization by a great variety of animals. Primitive animals have special cells which respond differentially to light: flatworms and snails can determine the difference between darkness and light; earthworms have cells that indicate not only shadows but also the direction of the object producing the shadow; among several marine organisms light produces a directional swimming reaction either toward the light or away from it. The source of light is not necessarily the sun or reflected light from the sky. Certain sandhoppers will orient to the moon just about as well as to the sun.

Cells that are sensitive to light become grouped together in a number of anatomical arrangements differing from group to group. Generally, they are called eyes, irrespective of the anatomical details. There is a great range from simple pigment spots to the complicated structure of the eye of the squid. Echinoderms have spots at various places on the body that indicate darkness or light. Among flagellates there are cups containing specially sensitive areas. Insects have compound eyes including a large number of independent cells which provide certain advantages in determining the direction of an object. The eye of the squid and of the vertebrate is an extremely complicated organ anatomically and provides a very clear resolution of the light rays. The lens of the vertebrate eye is very versatile. In some species the lens itself moves backward and forward, while in other vertebrates the shape of the lens changes. The primeval accomplishment of photoreceptors is to indicate a change in the amount of light. A higher development is the indication of the kind of light. One can consider that color detection is simply a refinement of the ability to pick up certain wavelengths. This refinement permits an animal to detect additional detail about its environment.

Light rays that are perceived by animals usually are reflected from some object. True, some light is perceived directly from the sun, but these rays indicate only that it is daytime (secondary meanings are direction and time of day). However, light that is reflected from an object tells the animal about the object after the animal has learned the meaning of particular configurations of wavelengths. Certain midges are attracted to white surfaces and then to the edge—that is, the part having the greatest contrast.

We noted that animals commonly developed the ability to produce chemicals that serve as stimuli. A few animals have developed the ability to produce light. The information usually indicates to other members the location of an individual fish. Fireflies, in contrast, produce light as a signal in courtship behavior.

Light rays by their physical properties are peculiarly adapted to indicate movement as well as location. Thus, light accentuated by movement is a major means of sending information to another member of the species. Elaborate courtship performances of birds, using brilliant colors and peculiar movements, transmit information to another bird. To emphasize the advantages of light over chemicals, contrast the success of sending semaphore signals with the difficulty of using chemicals to transmit information rapidly in perfect temporal order over a long distance.

The sense of touch is a simple mechanical response to pressure at close range. Many animals have special cells or groups of cells that respond to pressure. Crustaceans have on various parts of the body hairs that are attached to nerves, and when these hairs are moved, pressure sends impulses. Often free nerve endings give a generalized response. Touch provides information about the immediate environment.

Hearing is a kind of mechanical sense that has developed in higher animals and utilizes air waves for obtaining information about the environment. Hearing appears in advanced arthropods and in all vertebrates. It is rare among invertebrates, although possibly some animals are able to react as a whole to air waves. Anatomically the organs of hearing become very complicated and diversified. Among the vertebrates there is little variety; the organ is nearly always located in the head and generally is connected closely to the organs of equilibrium. Fish show a modification in connections with the air bladder through a series of small bones which may increase the ability to pick up waves of pressure. Among the arthropods the location of the hearing organ is varied: it appears on the leg of the locust, on the tails of some crustaceans (mysids), and in the antennules of some of the decapods. The anatomical details of the organ differ considerably among these groups. Hearing, of course, is a means of long-distance detection of environmental cues. Its major use is detection of other animals rather than the condition of the environment. So, for example, sounds indicate the location of prey or an enemy or a mate rather than a condition of the environment. A robin listens for an earthworm, but an earthworm does not listen for the pH of the soil. Thus, hearing may be considered as the most highly advanced sense modality.

An important aspect in hearing is the fact that many of the sounds are made by animals. It is true that some responses occur to sounds from the environment, such as wind. But generally the sound is produced by another animal. For example, certain female wasps make sounds by chewing their way out of the ground. The males respond to this noise. However, the noise is not specific for each species, so males from three species appear and must use another stimulus to determine which females belong to their own species. The sounds made by vertebrates are commonplace. They serve for information about courtship or danger.

Evolution

The preceding descriptions of the senses have given an indication of the use of senses from the behavioral viewpoint. The anatomical details have been mentioned only briefly since they are relatively well known and readily available in textbooks, some of which are named at the end of this chapter. From the viewpoint of behavior the anatomical details are not vitally important except as the accuracy or acuity of the organ is affected. Throughout the animal kingdom there seems to be a steady progression in complexity of the organs parallel to a change in the function. Among the lowest invertebrates the sense organs detect primarily conditions of the environment. The amoeba detects acetic acid in a bowl, many marine forms detect light and dark, and numerous other forms are sensitive to temperature. However, among the higher arthropods and among the vertebrates more elaborate senses develop to facilitate detection of members of the same species or of other animals. Thus, as one proceeds up the evolutionary scale, one realizes that the environment is becoming less important relatively and that the members of the same species or of different species are assuming greater significance to the lives of the individuals. Devices develop to notify other members of a species of the presence and location of individuals, with the result that mating is facilitated. Among insects, for example, the development of sound and hearing has greatly facilitated bringing together the two sexes. Among the vertebrates and even some arthropods an additional function—namely, the use of senses to detect a competitor—is added. This ability becomes most important in birds and mammals. Especially in birds, song and, of course, the sense of hearing are vitally important in the arrangement of the social organization, as will be seen in Chapter 5. However, even among the arthropods there are sounds, such as the rasping produced by a crab in defense of its burrow, which serve to notify another individual of competition. Naturally, development of the use of organs for detecting other individuals must be preceded or accompanied by the development of some means of producing signals. Some of the higher forms have elaborate means of producing sound. Insects may vibrate their wings or rub one object against another. Fish have a variety of means of producing sounds, and, as is well known, both birds and mammals have elaborate vocal apparatus. For species that use a sense to detect other members of the species, the means for production of sound is an integral part of the behavioral apparatus.

In addition to the production of sound to utilize the sense of hearing, there is the development of elaborate structural devices to utilize the sense of vision. Birds in particular have developed types of plumage and special structures that serve to identify visually the sex or courtship condition of an individual. This same function is performed by the large claw in the fiddler crab and by a number of other structures among insects.

Recently the production of chemical substances that affect another member of the species have attracted attention. These substances have the name phaeromones, in an analogy to the name hormones. In general, these chemicals, produced by one member of the species, influence through the chemical sense of smell the behavior of another individual. Some are well known, such as the production by female moths of odorous materials that can attract the males literally for many miles. More recently, phaeromones have been detected in a number of species including mammals. For example, a male mouse that is strange to a female may, through odor, have a deleterious effect on pregnancy. The detection by a male dog of the female in heat is, of course, a well-known example of the use of a chemical by one individual to communicate information to another.

Oftentimes more than one stimulus is used to detect an object. Some crabs do not use vision to detect food but respond to both tactile and chemical stimuli. Indeed, the combination results in a greater response than either sense alone.

It needs to be noted that some stimuli come directly from the object that is utilized by the animal. An item of food emits stimuli, either chemical or visual, that serve to bring the animal directly to it. Conversely, noxious chemicals serve directly to warn the individual. However, in other cases a stimulus becomes a symbol of an action rather than of the particular object. Birds, it is now known, can

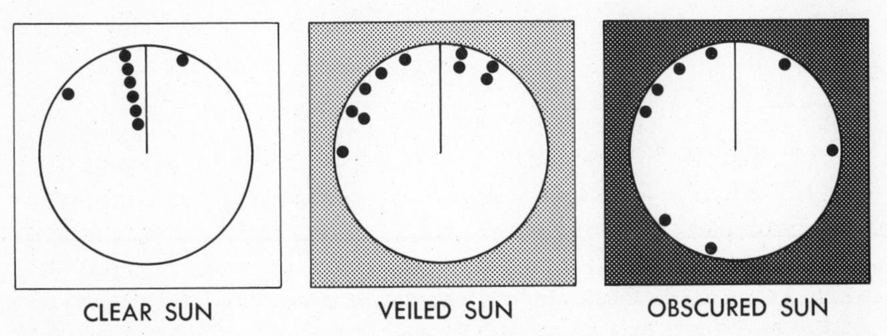

Figure 2·2. Importance of sun in orientation of Adelie Penguins released near South Pole. The circle represents the birds' horizon. The rookery was in the direction of the vertical line. The dots represent the direction of each bird on the horizon. When the sun was veiled or obscured, the birds were unable to orient toward their rookery. [From J. T. Emlen and R. Penny, in *The Ibis,* **106,** 1964.]

orient according to the direction of the sun (Figure 2·2) and even to the location of stars. The birds obviously do not use either the sun or the stars for their existence but simply take advantage of the stability of the location of these objects and the regularity of their changes to attain a particular direction which eventually will bring them to places where food and other requisites are available. A less spectacular example is the presence of warning colors on distasteful insects. The predatory bird does not directly taste the insect, at least after the first time, but is warned away by the elaborate color scheme. This shift in the meaning of stimuli is analogous to the conditioned reflex in which the significance of an object is transferred to some other signal. To carry out this analogy one can point out that the dog in the classical conditioning experiment does not eat the bell but the bell signifies that food is coming. Thus, the chemical sense of the dog has been replaced by the sound of the bell. To return to the example of using the sun as a means of obtaining information, it is in a sense a long-distance sense modality, since it indicates the location of important objects at a distance of hundreds of miles.

In concluding this brief and unconventional discussion of the senses, we can note that animals are extremely well equipped with a wide variety of anatomical and physiological structures for indicating to the individual the important circumstances of its environment. Furthermore, it must be noted that these conditions and procedures are constantly evolving, that new physical attributes of the environment have been taken advantage of through the evolutionary scale. Indeed, man is continuing this evolution by developing the use of such things as radio waves for obtaining and communicating information.

References

Buddenbrock, Wolfgang von. *The Senses.* Ann Arbor: University of Michigan Press, 1960. 167 pp.

Fraenkel, G. S., and D. I. Gunn. *The Orientation of Animals.* New York: Dover Press, 1964 (reprint of 1940 edition).

Kare, Marley R., and Bruce P. Halpern (eds.). *The Physiological and Behavioral Aspects of Taste.* Chicago: University of Chicago Press, 1961. xvi + 149 pp.

Lanyon, W. E., and W. N. Tavolga (eds.). *Animal Sounds and Communication.* Washington, D.C.: Amer. Inst. Biol. Sciences, 1960. xiii + 443 pp.

Lissman, H. W. "Proprioceptors," in "Physiological Mechanisms in Animal Behaviour," *Symp. Soc. Exp. Biol., 4*:34–59 (1950).

Zotterman, Y. (ed.). *Olfaction and Taste.* New York: The Macmillan Company, 1963. ix + 396 pp.

CHAPTER

3

Adjustment to Habitat

IN THE PRECEDING CHAPTERS we have seen that the welfare (and hence survival) of animals depends upon detection of the nature of their habitat and subsequent action. This chapter will consider in more detail the nature of the habitat, the features that must be detected, and the possibilities of action that will aid survival. We will see that animals have many problems to solve; that they develop a variety of behaviors in the solution of these problems. Distantly related animals often develop essentially the same solution to a given problem. We will note a trend away from the adjustment by the individual to the habitat and toward the adjustment by the entire population to the habitat conditions.

Basic Law of Adjustment

Before considering the parts of the habitat in detail, it is necessary to consider a basic law concerning the relation of animals to habitat. Almost a century ago, Liebig proposed a law which has come to be known as the law of the minimum. His work dealt primarily with plants but can be extended to include animals also. He called attention to the fact that for a short range as the supply of some essential nutrient increases, the growth of a plant will correspond to the increase of nutrient. In other words, growth of the plant had been determined or limited by the supply of the nutrient, since variations in the amount of nutrient result in a change in the growth. The particular nutrient is called a limiting factor; this factor is available at the minimum that will allow a particular growth. Consider Figure 3·1. Several plants in identical pots receive some nutrient in graded quantities and grow accordingly. However, above some particular level (arrow) an increase of nutrient has no effect and no longer *limits* the growth; some other factor (perhaps water) has become limiting. Beyond this amount the particular nutrient no longer limits the growth, for a change has no effect on the growth.

This law of the minimum has over the past century been extended to many different organisms and situations. Numerous complications and restrictions have been found, but in general the law can

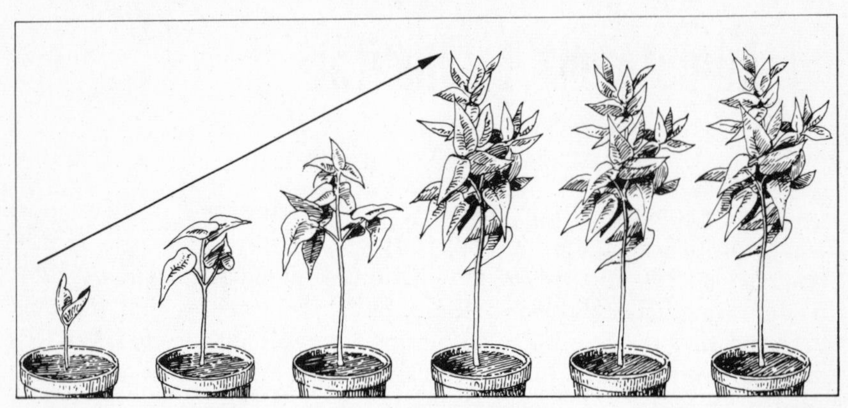

Increasing Nutrient

Figure 3·1. A simplified illustration of the limiting effect of a nutrient on growth. Up to the arrowhead the nutrient controls or limits growth; beyond the arrowhead some other factor takes over.

be said to apply to a large number of relationships. Some of the exceptions to the validity of this law occur at the extremes of its range just as is true of any such law—the law of gravity, for example. From the law of the minimum it follows that in a general way animals respond to a particular part of their environment for at least a short period of time when that part is limiting. Consider the case of our dog. His behavior is determined by a sequence of factors acting according to definite relationships. If the dog is in a cold place, he can produce enough heat to keep warm for a while, but eventually he will have to do something to maintain his warmth. Since there are numerous factors in the environment, it is obvious that the particular limiting factor will vary from time to time and from place to place. Under natural conditions there is a bewildering shift of limitation by factors, so that in many cases it becomes essentially impossible in nature to know what is happening. Nevertheless, it is profitable to recognize that animals are restricted in their behavior by specific factors that act according to a general rule.

The characteristics of the habitat of animals are known to everyone in a general way and will not be described in great detail here. The texts on ecology, listed at the end of this chapter, give extensive details. In general, the habitat always serves two major needs: (1) substrate for support; (2) substrate for movement.

SUPPORT. Water is a major habitat of animals and certainly is the most primitive of environments. It has a number of advantages. Since it is dense enough for support but not too dense for penetration, animals have in it a continuous environment in all directions. They are not confronted with as many problems as are found at an interface between two substrates. It is, of course, recognized that some forms do live at the interface of water and soil or of water and air. However, these forms have developed new means of coping with the environmental problems. Another advantage of water is its provision of a stable environment. The physical properties of water happen to have characteristics that prevent rapid changes in temperature. For these reasons water provides a very satisfactory and stable substrate.

Land, in contrast, provides a rather different substrate. It is obviously more solid and therefore presents animals with different problems. Animals generally live on the surface of land and so are confronted with accommodation to an interface either between land and air or land and water. Thus, the individual animal must adjust to two different kinds of substrate as well as to an interface. A second feature about land is its physical and chemical variability from place to place. The nature of the surface, the presence or absence of chemical nutrients, the temperature, and many other features may change over relatively short distances. Because of these changes aimals must make a greater variety of adjustments when living on land than in water.

Air is still a third type of substrate and, like water, can completely surround the animal. However, air is not sufficiently dense to provide satisfactory support for an animal or for its reproductive products. For this reason animals sooner or later must come to land or water for their essential physiological and reproductive functions. In a few cases animals have developed the ability to survive in air for long periods. The sooty tern apparently does not alight from the time it leaves its breeding place till it returns. Young birds apparently fly or soar over the tropical oceans for four years, the age at first breeding. Air is even more labile in temperature and other characteristics and thus does not provide a satisfactory medium for animal habitat.

MOVEMENT. The second feature in the substrate important to animals is the need for means to move about. With some exceptions animals, in contrast to plants, have developed methods of moving about to find their essential needs rather than simply waiting for the essentials of life to be brought to them. Some primitive forms merely float in the water and if lucky passively receive suitable nutrients. Under these circumstances, the physical conditions, such as temperature, and the chemical conditions, such as nutrients and oxygen, come passively to any animal able to utilize them at the time. However, since such a delivery system may be very irresponsible, animals developed a wide variety of means to move to places where they may find better conditions. Even very primitive forms have developed a system of getting somewhere else. One of these, the hydra, never knows where it is going because it does not have any real sense organs. However, if conditions are bad in one place, there is always the chance of their being better elsewhere, and so the hydra simply takes off.

The higher forms, as is well known, have developed means of obtaining their environmental requisites by swimming, walking, running, or flying. Many forms have developed an ability to swim, which functionally augments the advantages of being in a moving medium but is less subject to the vagaries of chance. Swimming has, of course, developed independently in large numbers of animals; some (certain mammals) have descended from terrestrial forms. Generally, swimming is the result of propulsion by a tail or by fins. In some forms (squid) a jet mechanism is used, but it is not very satisfactory for it tends to be too jerky. Although very fast, it does not have the possibilities of easy adjustment of speed.

Walking and running have developed in many animals by using protrusions of some sort from the body. The essential means, of course, is to alternate movement and support on different legs. The mechanical arrangements and nervous control become very elaborate. Incidentally, no animal has invented a wheel for movement (although some animals roll).

The most complicated form of movement is flying, a term that may by broadened to include gliding also. Many kinds of birds and insects have developed the ability to fly. Flight has the distinct advantages of being very rapid and of covering long distances with a small expenditure of energy. Thus, flying animals are able to get from one habitat to another both rapidly and cheaply in terms of energy.

From the preceding summary we see that animals have developed many means of movement from one place to another where there may be a better supply of their requirements. Now, let us consider the types of requirements that an animal must find.

MAINTAIN LIFE. The first big category may be called maintenance requirements and includes such obvious features as food, water, and oxygen. No species receives its requirements purely by a chance or random event. However, many species have only minor abilities to alter the chance provision by the environment. Many protozoa have little ability to move. Others (paramecium) can actually produce a current of water which brings requisites to the animal. A metazoan, the jellyfish, floats and to a large degree takes what comes by chance, simply by staying on the surface and directing its movements to a limited extent. Many parasites leave things more or less to chance by dropping their eggs or larvae in large numbers at random; thus some settle in an area suitable for living. Actually, however, provision of the suitable host requirements is not completely left to chance, since the hosts tend to inhabit the area where these eggs have been dropped. Other parasites seem to find their hosts largely by random wandering without real direction. Certain animals have developed elaborate devices for securing objects, and place them in a situation where the results really depend upon chance. Spiders, for example, have developed fantastic webs and yet depend largely on chance for the kinds of insects caught in these masterpieces. Even here the spider does not leave everything to chance but puts his web in a place where it is likely that some insects will pass.

From the preceding discussion we see that in some forms the element of chance is very great. But we also see that some type of choice by the animal is nearly always present. Searching has become an important means of finding the environmental requisites, and elaborate equipment for searching has been developed. In some cases, such as the hydra, searching is largely random because sense organs are absent; but in other cases, such as insects and vertebrates, searching is largely directional through communications from the sense organs. However, in contrast to searching by moving under the direction of sense organs is searching by bringing large quantities of the environment to the individual. This process is used by bivalve molluscs which search their environment by sucking large quantities of water through an apparatus which takes out the desirable substances. The bivalve molluscs thus are generally sedentary and need only limited possibilities of movement. Copepods also illustrate this type of behavior by straining fantastic quantities of water in their search for plankton. A more venturesome type of searching is performed by a crab (*Cardiosoma*) living on beaches in Florida. It notices by sight almost any object falling within about 10 feet and goes to it whether it be food or not. The crabs also respond to a sound. Thus, at this stage of evolution the animal responds but not selectively; it wastes a lot of energy pouncing on things that are not food.

The chase and capture procedure is a further stage in obtaining an animal's maintenance requirements. Clearly this stage requires the most elaborate sense organ and motion equipment. The chase and capture method, however, is apparent in the very earliest forms, even those with only modest equipment. The amoeba is able to move about and literally to chase and capture food particles. The hydra can capture animals through its tentacles but, of course, is unable to chase them because of its slow movement and lack of means of perception. Certain snails are able to burrow through the sand and in this way capture their food requirements. A more spectacular example of this process is the behavior of the squid in chasing and capturing very fast swimming fish. The squid, of course, has very elaborate sense organs and locomotor means. The ability of vertebrates and insects to chase and capture is well known and again depends on sensory equipment and an ability to move. Consider the barn owl, which has such highly developed and coordinated sense organs that it can in pitch dark detect by sounds the location and movement of a mouse and accurately aim its claws to capture it.

Reproduce Life. Maintenance of life is, of course, only part of the problem of adjustment to the habitat. In addition, it is necessary that the habitat provide a suitable means of reproduction for the survival of the species. In general, habitat requirements for reproduction must be compatible with the maintenance requirements; otherwise, the individual itself could not survive. However, from the viewpoint of continuation of the species it is necessary that reproduction occur, and if a number of individuals are sacrificed in the process, no harm is done as long as the species is perpetuated. At the simplest level one can consider a chance meeting of male and female gametes of marine invertebrates. Under these circumstances there are no real habitat requirements, since the substrate, usually water, takes care of the arrangement. Moving water, of course, increases the chances of meeting of the egg and sperm. The coelenterates and echinoderms put millions of gametes into the water, and some of these eventually meet. Actually, the situation is not completely left to chance, since in the first place the males and female tend to be in similar locations, and, second, the discharge of gametes is somewhat synchronized in some of the echinoderms. Furthermore, there seem to be certain responses, presumably on a chemical basis, of the sperm to the egg. Other forms such as certain annelids (*Nereis*) use what is basically a chance method but improve the chances by the timing. These worms may produce sperm and eggs only at a particular time of year. The famous palolo worms apparently come to the surface in large numbers at a particular phase of the moon and thereby increase very greatly the chances of meeting. Molluscs, on the other hand, rely on currents to bring sperm to the female. But again reproduction is not left to chance, since these currents are greatly accentuated by the siphons of the molluscs.

Many forms of fish also have devices for ensuring that eggs and sperm have an opportunity to meet. Forms such as haddock produce vast quantities of eggs and sperm more or less simultaneously. Under these circumstances, the likelihood of fertilization is greatly increased. In considering the number of chance meetings, it needs to be remembered that the frequency of occurrence of a highly improbable event can be numerically increased by increasing the number of opportunities. Thus, the number of times an egg meets a sperm depends on np, where n is the number of sperm and p is the probability of meeting. Clearly, even though the probability be extremely low, if the numbers are high, then some contacts will occur. Also note that it is advantageous to produce eggs and sperm in approximately equal numbers, unless one sex has a special device to increase the value of p. Since, from an energy viewpoint, it is inefficient to produce large numbers of gametes, through the millions of years a wide variety of behavioral devices have been developed that reduce the chance element in meeting—that is, to increase the value of p. Consider a mollusc that relies on chance meeting of sperm and egg. If the probability of meeting is 0.002, then 500 sperm must be produced to ensure one meeting. The number of meetings can be doubled by increasing sperm to 1,000 or by increasing the probability to 0.004.

A major means for increasing the probability of meeting is selection of an area where other individuals may be present. Obviously this selection depends upon some means of detecting the area and of getting there or, at least, staying there. Thus, for example, a burrowing polychaete (*Owenia*) inhabits a sandy type of locality. Since these worms are fairly well restricted to this area, the chance of meeting a reproductive individual is increased. The larvae of parasites are usually distributed in areas where the host is likely to occur, and so the larvae have a good chance of finding a host and being able to reproduce. The most spectacular example of selection of an area is the development, especially in birds, of territorial behavior. Under these circumstances, the male finds an area suitable for raising young, and the female has a guarantee that both mate and suitable habitat are available.

Still another means of increasing the efficiency of reproduction is the development of devices to find the other sex. This behavior requires organs to perceive the other sex as well as a means of reaching it. Such procedures are numerous and require only a few examples. Many invertebrates put into the water, with the gametes, chemicals that diffuse through the medium and notify other individuals that gametes are available. Many insects have an elaborate series of sound signals indicating to the female the location of the male. The familiar call of the cicada in summer is an example. Here the efficiency of meeting is high. Numerous male fish prepare

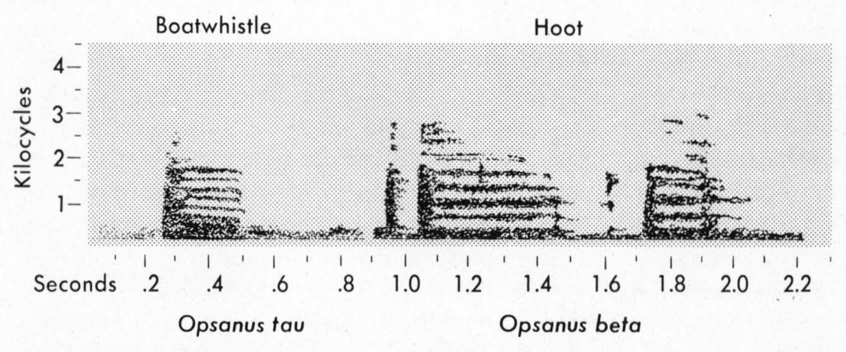

Figure 3·2. Spectrograph of sounds made by fish (toadfish), presumably to locate other individuals. [From H. Winn, in W. N. Tavolga (ed.), *Marine Bio-Acoustics*, New York: Pergamon Press, 1964.]

nest sites where the female can lay her eggs with a high probability that they will be fertilized. The songs of birds and probably some fish sounds (Figure 3·2) are means of finding the other sex. The efficiency of fertilization in many cases is further increased by anatomical devices. It is not enough simply to find the other sex. The gametes must also meet. Organs of copulation increase even more the likelihood that the gametes will come together. These organs include various devices that first orient the male to the female in the proper position and, second, ensure that the sperm and egg are placed close together. An interesting accentuation of efficiency occurs in hermaphrodites which, of course, have both sexes within the same individual; and when one hermaphrodite finds another, double reproduction may occur.

A final environmental requisite for reproduction is a supply of materials necessary for raising the young. Spectacular examples of such material requirements are the hives of bees and the nests of fish and of birds. To prepare these structures the animal must be able to perceive the features of its environment and to do something about it. Usually the actions involve the carrying of materials to some particular place and the molding of them into a structure. It is abundantly clear that this type of behavior requires a very high level of integration and results from a long sequence of evolution.

PROTECT LIFE. Another aspect of the environment necessary for the success of individuals is protection. Again, we can consider the simplest situation—namely, that animals survive by chance avoidance of harmful situations. Such occasions seem to be relatively rare, although some examples can be cited as approximations. The amoeba backs away from harmful objects, but it does not have any elaborate devices for protection. Among the higher vertebrates some situations can be described. For example, the caribou so seldom meets a wolf that it generally ignores its presence because the wolf cannot capture an alert caribou. However, occasionally a caribou and a wolf meet in a gully by chance, and under these circumstances, the wolf is usually able to kill the caribou.

Protection of an animal is more generally obtained by living in a safe type of habitat. Most forms have some sort of protection. They may burrow in holes in the ground, live under bushes or dense vegetation, or use a number of other structural devices. An additional development relating somewhat indirectly to the habitat is the use of protective coloration. Many birds and insects have developed coloration closely resembling the habitat. Under these circumstances, the behavior of the animal must be organized first to select the place where its coloration actually does resemble the habitat and, second, it must remain motionless and so escape detection. An apparent exception to protection may be mentioned. The South American bellbird depends on complete visibility. These birds are totally white and spend a major part of their time on a conspicuous perch in the treetops. Under these circumstances, they have command of the situation and are able to avoid danger, by flight when necessary.

The ultimate level of efficiency in animal protection is perhaps the ability to escape from trouble. The individual must be in a habitat where detection of a predator and rapid escape are possible.

Some worms which live in tubes in the mud are able to detect the approach of a predator and quickly retire into the safety of their tubes. Other forms depend on speed to escape and to leave the predator far behind. However, in these cases the animals must be in an open habitat where visibility is good and where speed will be an advantage. Some animals use additional devices to confuse the predator. The squid ejects a cloud of black ink, and scallops emit offensive chemicals. Woodpeckers give special calls.

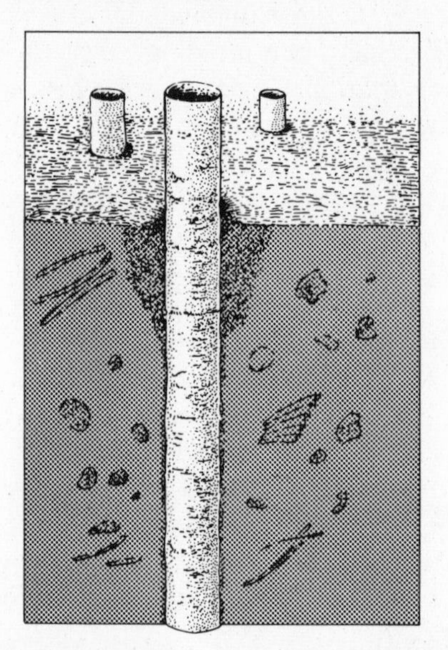

Figure 3·3. Tubes, built by polychaete worms, protruding from mud. The part of the tube shown is about a third of an inch long. [From R. D. Barnes, in *Biological Bulletin,* **127** (3), 1964.]

While it is, of course, obvious that animals must be able to find and reach a favorable habitat, it is also necessary that they be able to detect and avoid a harmful habitat. This process, of course, occurs throughout the animal kingdom. The amoeba reacts to a strong light or heat or harmful chemicals by moving away. The hydra can turn somersaults to get away from an unsatisfactory location. Among the vertebrates many individuals successfully avoid extreme conditions in the habitat.

Habitat Factors

During this discussion we have been taking for granted the reader's acquaintance with the various factors of the habitat to which an animal must react. These topics are discussed in great detail in many ecological texts (see references). For our present purposes it is desirable to mention some of these factors since the succeeding chapters will show how an animal's behavior has succeeded in adjusting to these conditions. One can consider first the physical factors. Temperature of the surroundings is extremely important and is particularly variable, especially in the air environment. Therefore, animals need equipment for prompt detection of temperature. For example, certain snails selected a temperature of 21°–26°C when given a range of 6°–36°C. Deaths occurred at 40°C. Humidity resembles temperature in being a characteristic of the surroundings of terrestrial animals. The snails selected a substrate with a moisture content of 50–80 per cent. Light and other wavelengths of radiation are important to the animal through their effects on energy. Certain wavelengths can be extremely harmful to parts of the organism. Barometric pressure is rarely important for terrestrial forms, but hydrostatic pressure may be of critical value for aquatic forms. Gravity is a different type of factor rarely, if ever, harmful as such, yet extremely valuable and necessary in indicating to the animal its actual position. Other physical factors of a rather different sort include precipitation, important primarily in controlling the plants in the habitat and thereby providing food and shelter. Precipitation per se is rarely important to animals except under such unusual circumstances as hail storms or hurricanes. Another aspect of the physical environment that should be mentioned is the action of waves, tides, and currents which, through their physical action, may damage or move animals about. Oftentimes the animals have developed adaptations to take advantage of these features.

Another big category of habitat conditions may be called chemical, using the term in a broad sense. Normally, these features include the necessary nutrients and substances for maintenance. The gases (oxygen) and the food, minerals, and grit must be available in suitable quantities. Another type of habitat feature that must be considered is salinity. For appropriate relationships to the environment the chemical composition must be such that no significant changes in the organism result from chemical reactions with the environment. A final category of factors of the habitat is structural and includes living or nesting places, shelter or protective situations, and lastly, what might be termed psychological requirements. Song perches that seem to be necessary in some birds for the proper fulfillment of territorial functions would be included in this category.

From this quick survey of the habitat conditions one can say that animals need to make a wide variety of choices and adjustments, which they do through their behavior. The result of all of these circumstances is that animals have occupied a wide variety of ecological niches. This variety is based on the ability of animals to detect their environmental conditions and to do something about their needs. An aspect that has not received adequate attention is the significance of larval stages in providing flexibility of relationships to the environment. Larval forms may have very different ecological needs from the adult forms and are able to maintain the species at a high level of abundance in habitats that may not be suitable for adult stages. Under these circumstances, the behavioral flexibility of the several stages in the life cycle greatly enhances the possibilities of survival. Another feature to be remembered is that the animals react to some specific stimulus, not to the whole conglomeration of environmental factors. Thus, a nestling bird will respond by opening its beak to tapping the edge of the nest, a stimulus that is normally only produced by an adult bringing food. The nestling does not respond to all the stimuli from the adult, only certain ones. Oftentimes, therefore, animals act in a nonsensical manner simply because accidentally a stimulus occurred but at the wrong time or place.

It is rather surprising that learning and conditioning have a relatively small role in the entire animal kingdom. Most of the actions of animals are a reflex type, although some kinds of special conditioning or learning are now being detected in very primitive forms. However, the possibility of continual modification and adjustment of reactions to the habitat is a very recent feature in evolution. Clearly, these possibilities greatly enhance the efficiency of the species.

An aspect that will be noted again and again in this book is the existence of convergence in behavior among widely diversified animals. When confronted with a habitat problem, different kinds of animals tend to behave in the same way. For example, the capture of prey or the escape from a predator has many similarities among insects and vertebrates. The anatomical organs are, of course, very different, but the behavioral problems are solved in very much the same way. Another example of convergence in terms of behavior is the development of territorial actions among large numbers of vertebrates and even among invertebrates. Again, the habitat problem has been solved in behavioral manners that are very similar even though the anatomical and physiological equipment is radically different.

References

Andrewartha, H. G. *Introduction to the Study of Animal Populations.* Chicago: University of Chicago Press, 1961. xvii + 281 pp.

Clarke, George L. *Elements of Ecology.* New York: John Wiley & Sons, 1954. xiv + 534 pp.

Cloudsley-Thompson, J. L. *Rhythmic Activity in Animal Physiology and Behaviour.* New York: Academic Press, 1961. 236 pp.

Dice, Lee R. *Natural Communities.* Ann Arbor: University of Michigan Press, 1952. x + 547 pp.

Green, James. *The Biology of Crustacea.* Chicago: Quadrangle Books, Inc., 1961. xv +180 pp.

Harlow, Harry F., and Clinton N. Woolsey (eds.). *Biological and Biochemical Bases of Behavior.* Madison: University of Wisconsin Press, 1958. xx + 476 pp.

Lack, David. *The Natural Regulation of Animal Numbers.* London: Oxford University Press, 1954. viii + 343 pp.

Nicol, J. A. Colin. *The Biology of Marine Animals.* New York: Interscience Publishers, Inc., 1960. xi + 707 pp.

Odum, Eugene P. *Fundamentals of Ecology.* Philadelphia: W. B. Saunders Company, 1959. xvii + 546 pp.

Smythe, R. H. *Animal Habits. The Things Animals Do.* Springfield, Ill.: Charles C. Thomas, 1963.

CHAPTER

4

Emancipation from Environment

IN THE PRECEDING CHAPTER we saw that each animal lives in a relatively special place, that its requirements are relatively rigid, and that various senses help it to find its suitable place. The finding of a place is a combination of searching behavior and reacting to what the sense modalities tell the animal about the environment. We should avoid the supposition that all animals are necessarily well adapted to their environment. Indeed, we can note some spectacular cases in which the animal survives in spite of its poor relationship to the various features of its habitat. What could be worse for going through mud than the hooves of a pig?

Adaptation to the habitat is accomplished in several ways. A basic source of adjustment is provided by sexuality. A species having more than one sex has the opportunity for recombination of various hereditary characteristics producing perhaps the well-known hybrid vigor or increasing the likelihood of new traits. The presence of several sexes gives a species a likelihood of greater variability and hence greater chance of survival when the habitat changes. However, it is obviously necessary for the sexes to meet in order that fertilization may occur. The meeting of the sexes is, of course, brought about through various behavioral devices that ensure that several individuals get together. We are accustomed to thinking in terms of two sexes but three or more sexes are theoretically possible. In fact, more than two sorts of sexes occur in some of the molds and protozoa. However, the probability of meeting is, of course, the product of the several probabilities of being at a particular place at a particular time. A unisexual form, of course, has no problem of meeting another individual. A bisexual form meets other individuals in proportion to the product of two probabilities. The trisexual form would meet according to the product of the three probabilities of being in a particular place. Thus, if the probability that an animal is in a particular place at a particular time is .600, then the probability that two animals will be there is .360 and the probability that three animals will be there is .216. Continuation of this argument shows clearly that a species requiring four or more sexes would have a very low probability of accomplishing mating. Under these circumstances, the greatly increased variability possible with four or more sexes would be prevented by the low likelihood of the four sexes getting together simultaneously. This discussion of the probability of meeting by various sexes is introductory to later comments in various chapters concerning the probabilities of an animal's finding a suitable environment. It will be seen that the behavior of animals consists, in large part, of devices for increasing the probability that members of two sexes get together in a suitable habitat.

Selection of Habitat

In the present chapter we will discuss in some detail the ways individual animals select their habitat. An individual animal is surrounded by a variety of conditions; some of these conditions are suitable for the particular physiological and anatomical configuration of the individual, many unsuitable. If we state that the probability of a suitable condition is P_1 and the probability of another suitable condition is P_2, and so on, we can state that the probability of survival (P_s) of a species is the product of all of these probabilities. We can form an equation $P_s = P_1P_2P_3 \ldots P_n$, where n indicates the total number of conditions necessary for survival. To put this equation in everyday words, consider the survival of a woodchuck living in a field. Suppose that the likelihood of his finding water is very low, the likelihood of finding food is high, and the likelihood of surviving a parasitic infection is low. The probability of surviving will be the product of these conditions. Obviously, there are many other factors in the environment. Note that if any of those probabilities is zero, then the animal, of course, cannot survive. The supreme function of behavior is to permit the animal to get into a place where the probabilities of each or many of these factors is high. The animal gets to such a place by first locating it through its sense organs and then by moving toward it. Thus, behavior can be thought of as a means of detecting and attaining situations in which the probability of various factors necessary to survival is the highest. One might say that the animal maximizes the product of probabilities of its environmental conditions.

The first step in increasing these probabilities is detection of the appropriate conditions. For this purpose the original means probably were simple exterior nerve endings (Chapter 2), which are, of course, specialized cells for detection of the environmental conditions. These specialized nerve endings are found principally in the lower forms but do exist even in mammals. More elaborate organs developed in higher animals to detect the environmental conditions. Through this combination of organs the conditions of the environment are detected and messages are sent through the nerves to the muscles and other structures involved in movement. As animals developed evolutionarily, the nervous system tended to concentrate the messages in the brain and there coordinate and

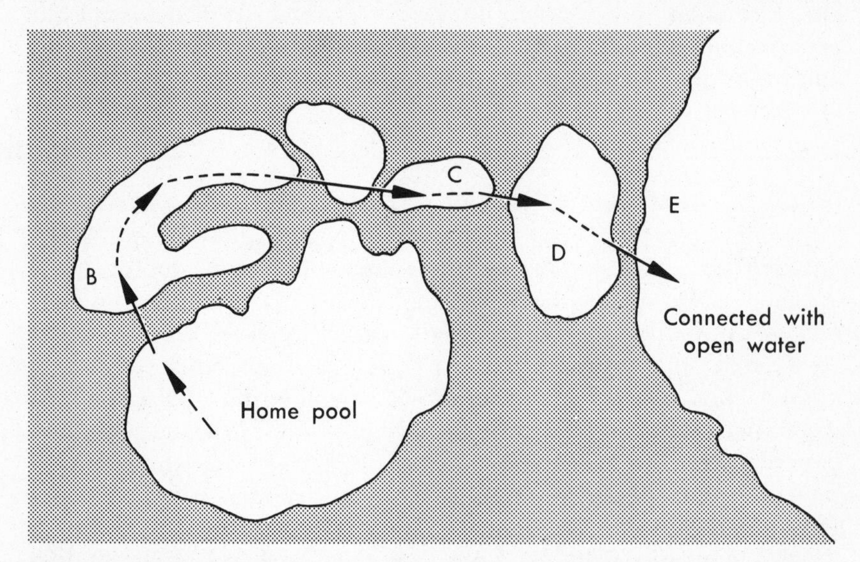

Figure 4·1. Jumps performed by a fish (goby) to get from pools to open water. When the fish's home pool dries up as the tide recedes, the fish jumps to *B, C, D,* and then to open water. It returns to the home pool at high tide. [From L. Aronson, *American Museum Novitates,* **1486,** 1951, published by The American Museum of Natural History.]

consolidate various signals. The earliest type of nerve system, of course, is simply a nerve net as found in hydra. The animal has to respond all or none to a stimulus in many situations. In the higher forms not only coordination but inhibition of messages also has developed.

Having received certain messages, the animal begins some sort of movement into a suitable habitat. The lowest types of animals usually respond to an adverse situation simply by leaving it. Thus, an amoeba exposed to acetic acid will simply move away. It is taking its chances on where it goes and so may find the environment is no better elsewhere, since it may have, for example, moved into a strong light. The amoeba will continue to move in one direction or another until it finds a suitable place. The higher forms, of course, have developed organs that can detect the conditions at a distance, so the randomness of the movements is reduced and the animal is able to find a suitable habitat quickly. For instance, among insects, the cluster flies are very adept at finding locations where a trace of warm air comes out of a building. They crawl through these little cracks and become a pest in our houses in the fall. As another example we can call attention to the fact that fish may be very sensitive to oxygen depletion and rapidly wander into other areas in search of a suitable concentration of oxygen, even jumping from one pool to another (Figure 4·1). Note that in the case of the cluster flies the animal was being attracted toward a particular condition, whereas in the case of the fish, the animal was getting away from a particular condition. As we shall see later, in many species learning

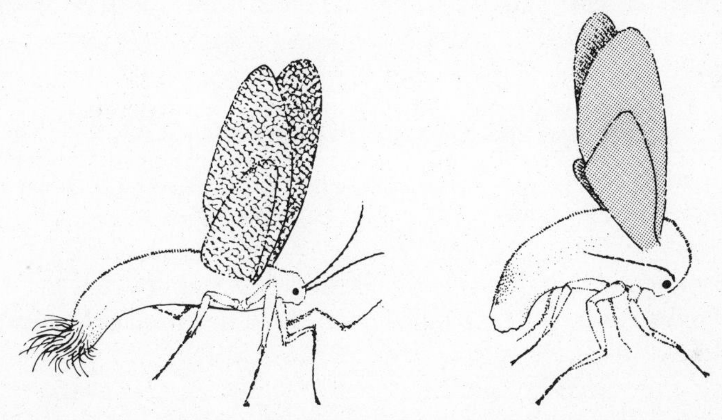

Figure 4·2. Protective postures of certain moths, presumably serving to repel predators. Note that the positions would not be confused with ordinary flight activity. [From A. D. Blest, in *Zoologica*, 49, 1964.]

becomes superimposed upon these conditions, so that the animal learns the characteristics or location of satisfactory situations and is able to go to such a place when it feels the need.

The avoidance of predators is another important behavior aspect. Actually, this problem is basically the same as avoidance of unsatisfactory conditions, but since the predator has a means of detecting and moving toward the animal, the prey has necessarily developed very elaborate behavior patterns to avoid predators. Some species avoid predators simply by speed after detection; others avoid predators by concealment, which, of course, amounts to preventing the predator from detecting the individual; still others overcome predators simply by bold action contrived to frighten or scare the predator away (Figure 4·2).

Emancipation from Habitat

The evolution of animals in terms of behavior has consisted very largely of the emancipation of the animal from dependence on the environment. In large part this emancipation has been the exclusion of harmful environmental features. Animals have also developed a means of finding the places most suitable for their special needs. The result of these behavioral features is that the probabilities mentioned have been very greatly increased. Consider as an example the probability of having sufficient oxygen. Animals in the ocean have a relatively stable supply of oxygen, but there are circumstances in which the supply is not adequate for a particular animal and it must either move or die. Thus, we can say that the probability of having enough oxygen is high, or something like 0.9. However, terrestrial animals have gotten into an environment where the oxygen supply, except at the very highest altitudes, is always adequate, and we can thus say that the probability of having enough oxygen is 1.0, or certainty. Under these circumstances, an animal no longer need worry about the oxygen supply and can devote its energies to other features. Clearly, the more environmental necessities with high probabilities, the easier it is for the animal to survive. The rest of this chapter will give examples of ways animals behave to emancipate themselves from the difficulties of the environment.

The very earliest form of life surely was a rare combination of organic molecules that survived because it could replace itself. This simple combination of molecules must have been entirely dependent upon the local environment, for presumably it had no means of detecting the specific conditions or of doing anything about them. Thus, it seems certain that chemical life originated and became extinct a multitude of times. However, some of these systems developed either a frequency or a stability that permitted them to begin to exclude some of the unsatisfactory environmental conditions. Perhaps these molecules somehow were located within a crevice of a rock or some other favorable situation which increased their probability of surviving. The molecules may have eventually developed some sort of wall and by this means made the first step in exclusion of the environment.

The first forms of life that are recognized as animals have definite cell walls, very thick in some cases. Because the walls must be porous to permit the entrance of chemical necessities, the animal already shows considerable choice based, naturally, on the available and necessary materials. Some of these unicellular organisms have developed special spores to permit survival through a particularly bad season. The spore, of course, is simply a means of setting up a very solid barrier against desiccation or some other aspect of the environment that would kill the normal cell. Thus, animals that have developed spores have invented a new system for emancipating themselves from poor conditions. Some of these unicellular animals have developed what are in effect sense organs to detect simple changes in the environment. So we see even in the extremely primitive animal the basic elements of behavior—namely, the ability to detect conditions and to do something about them.

Protective Structures. More highly developed animals have developed a wide variety of structures or solid walls providing excellent protection and hence increasing the probabilities of survival. We can mention some examples from several phyla among animals. Among the protozoan the dinoflagellates have developed a cellulose wall, a very effective protection against both environmental changes and predators. Also in this group the foraminifera have developed a surface structure called a test that is highly protective against the environment. Some coelenterates, the corals, have become colonial and developed means of laying down a stony protective layer, so that to all intents they are plants as far as behavior is concerned. The corals are, of course, classed as animals because they have descended from animals and must depend on plants for their energy sources. Another coelenterate, the hydroid, has produced a solid coating that also protects it from its environment.

Among the annelids a number of different devices exclude the environment. Worms, for example, secrete a mucous substance which is essentially a slimy protective coat serving several functions. It makes movement through the soil easier and also keeps away harmful substances. In addition, it perhaps serves to repel predators to a certain extent. A very primitive annelid, peripatus, living in the tropics has developed a heavy chitinous coating which serves very well to prevent destruction by predators and also to retain water in the dry season. Among the crustaceans, barnacles have devised a number of stony structures in which the animal exists fastened to a particular spot. Lobsters and crabs, with their very solid exoskeleton, are also in this group. Many molluscs have structures that exclude the environment. The gastropods have a coiled shell, and lamellibranches have valves that can be moved to permit the entrance of nutrients from the exterior. Even the cephalopods have a shell as a small relic of their ancestry. Polyzoa have developed independently a branching plantlike structure, another device to maintain the animal in exclusion from the changes in its environment. Even among the chordates the tunicates have protected themselves by the development of a cellulose body wall. The structures mentioned so far are all essentially skeletons which serve two functions. They support the animal and permit it to become somewhat larger than would be possible without a skeleton; but, perhaps more importantly, they protect the animal from changes in the environment.

Other animals have developed a device that may be more satisfactory than the skeleton because it is not an integral part of the animal. In a wide variety of phyla animals have attained an ability to construct a shelter. The possession of a shelter, of course, is advantageous to the animal since the animal is not restricted permanently to a situation, which can be abandoned if conditions necessitate. It is, of course, clear that a number of the cases already mentioned really are shelters, since the animal structure has become so large that the individual has become separated from it. For example, the barnacles secrete the shell as a definite part of their body but eventually it becomes independent.

As examples of the construction of shelters we can cite certain polychaetes which build tubes out of calcium carbonate. The tube is an external structure and serves as a home. The animal has even developed the ability to close a door, so to speak, on the top of the tube, further protecting itself from harm. As the animal grows, it can dissolve the tube and increase in size. The construction of tubes has permitted the development of group behavior among these worms. We can start the sequence with the solitary form, *Spirorbis,* which constructs a modest tube and lives widely separated from other individuals. The next stage perhaps is the aggregation where animals such as *Serpula* live close together. The final stage is a colonial one in which *Filograma* have connected tubes and so derive mutual benefit from their structures.

Burrows are another example of shelter construction. Coelenterates commonly burrow in the mud or sand bottom for protection against both predators and the environment. Burrows are, of course, widely used among the higher forms, especially mammals (Figure 4·3) and lizards, and serve the obvious functions. The ability to bore holes into solid objects to protect themselves from the environment has been developed in other forms. Many of the polychaete worms can bore into wood. The most spectacular cases are certain of the molluscs which can bore holes several feet into wood pilings and others that can dissolve limestone and bore a hole into it. Some of these structures are fantastic engineering achievements.

A number of species are not able to construct a shelter but have in contrast developed the habit of stealing a shelter belonging to some other form. The hermit crab is well known for its habit of getting into an abandoned shell of an aquatic snail and using this shelter. When the crab grows too large for the shell, it gets out and finds a larger one. An arthropod (*Phronomia*) parasitizes an ascidian and propels the house of the ascidian through the environment.

Still another way to avoid the difficulties encountered in the environment is to become parasitic. Actually, of course, the animal

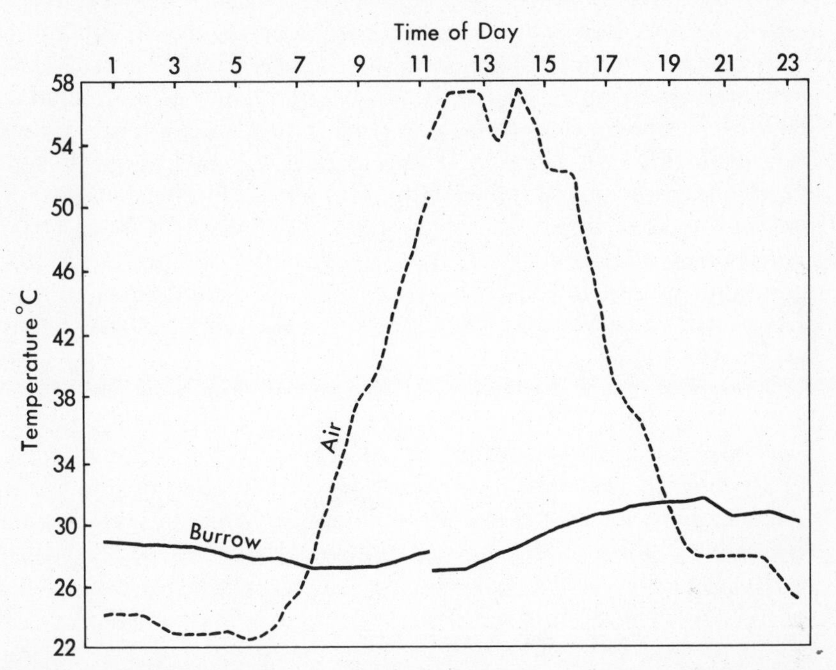

Figure 4·3. Relative stability of temperature in burrow of gopher (solid line) compared to that of air (dotted line). The construction of a burrow thus gives a gopher a more constant environment. [From T. E. Kennerly, in *Texas Journal of Science,* **16** (4), 1964.]

is not completely avoiding the environment, since that is impossible, but is trading a more variable environment for a less variable one. The parasite of the intestinal tract, for example, has a food supply readily available and also suitable conditions of acidity and of temperature. Under these circumstances, the animal has increased the probabilities of having the environmental necessities. The animal has avoided the difficulties of the environment, but it has multiplied difficulties in another direction—namely, finding the environment. Since an animal living parasitically has a tendency to reduce its anatomical structure, there has been a parallel reduction in the possibilities of behavior. Under these circumstances, parasites have lost many of the sense organs and much of their motility and thereby have increased the difficulty of finding a mate or a suitable environment. For these reasons the parasites have had to develop a program of fantastically high reproductive rates in order to maintain the species. It will be remembered that the number of occurrences of an event is the product of the likelihood of occurrences and the opportunities. Thus, an event that is highly improbable individually can occur if tried frequently enough. Behaviorally the parasites have permitted a great reduction in the likelihood of finding a mate or of finding a suitable place. However, they have compensated for this by a number of booster stages in reproduction. It is well known that large numbers of eggs are produced and that these eggs go through several stages. At each one of these stages the parasite multiplies many fold, increasing the number of individuals that find a suitable place. The parasites as a group have largely abandoned behavioral features in favor of a fantastically high rate of multiplication. Perhaps this abandonment of behavior started when they first used the shelter of a host to avoid the environment.

Dispersal from Shelter. The construction of a shelter accomplishes one objective—an increase in the probabilities of survival. But it goes contrary to another objective—the dispersal of the animal. Dispersal is necessary since the conditions at a particular place vary over a period of time, and the individuals at one spot will sooner or later be exterminated by some change in the environment. It is necessary for the survival of the species that individuals disperse into a wide variety of places to ensure that at all times some individuals will be in a favorable place. Clearly, the construction of a solid shelter reduces the likelihood of dispersal. Animals have solved this problem in many cases by the development of larval stages that disperse. Barnacles are perhaps the best example of this. The floating and swimming larvae float great distances in the ocean currents and eventually settle down to become adults. The gametes are another means for dispersal. In many cases the male and female gametes are placed in the aquatic environment and float freely or even swim about until fertilization and eventual establishment occur. In this manner many species have avoided the potentially disastrous effects of being confined to a particular spot because it provided shelter.

In a similar vein it needs to be recognized that animals must be able to get food and to avoid extremes. Animals confined to a shelter may have difficulty in getting food, since they cannot go after it. Also, they may need to avoid sudden extremes of environmental conditions. One obvious way to accomplish these tasks is to live in a uniform external medium such as water. Water through its unique physical properties has a number of attributes that make it surprisingly useful. Because it has a very high coefficient for heat, it changes temperature very slowly. Owing to its viscosity and density, water can support animals far better than can air, for example. Thus, many animals can exist in water under circumstances protecting them from rapid changes in the nature of the environment. Animals living in water are able to get food and are to a very large extent able to avoid extreme conditions.

HOMEOSTASIS. Another means of avoiding extremes and, at the same time, maintaining the possibility of getting food is the development of a uniform internal medium, obviously protected from external conditions by some device. The process of maintaining a relatively constant internal medium is known as homeostasis and comprises a very large part of the study of physiology. What has happened is that animals have developed a number of physiological and chemical means for maintaining the internal environment in a nearly constant state. These phenomena are not the primary concern of a book on animal behavior but should be recognized briefly as a very important consequence of the tendency of animals to emancipate themselves from the environment.

The physiological means that assist in homeostasis are very diverse. They are properly discussed in a number of physiological texts and also in books that emphasize the physiological aspect of behavior (see References at end of chapter). Here suffice it to say that these means are in part chemical, such as the concentration of salts in the blood stream; in part neurological, such as the changes brought about by nerve impulses; and in part endocrine, such as the messages sent through hormones to various parts of the body.

Behavior enters importantly into the problem of homeostasis since it can greatly reduce the extremes to which the homeostatic mechanisms must respond. Consider, for example, a lizard living in the desert. The lizard has a number of physiological means for maintaining its temperature at an appropriate level. Yet these means are unable to function adequately if the lizard is kept in sunlight, and the lizard promptly dies. In nature, it spends a large amount of time in the shade of whatever shelter is available, or it becomes, to a certain extent, nocturnal. In fact, a lizard rarely actually lives in the desert environment but avoids the extremes through behavior. Another case is the hibernation practiced by woodchucks and many other forms. These animals need a large amount of energy to get through the long winter period, but their food habits are such that they cannot obtain adequate food during the winter. Behavioral changes in the summer and fall result in the accumulation, through physiological processes, of large layers of fat. Then they go into a burrow and spend the winter there almost completely protected from the environment. A drop in body temperature is one of a number

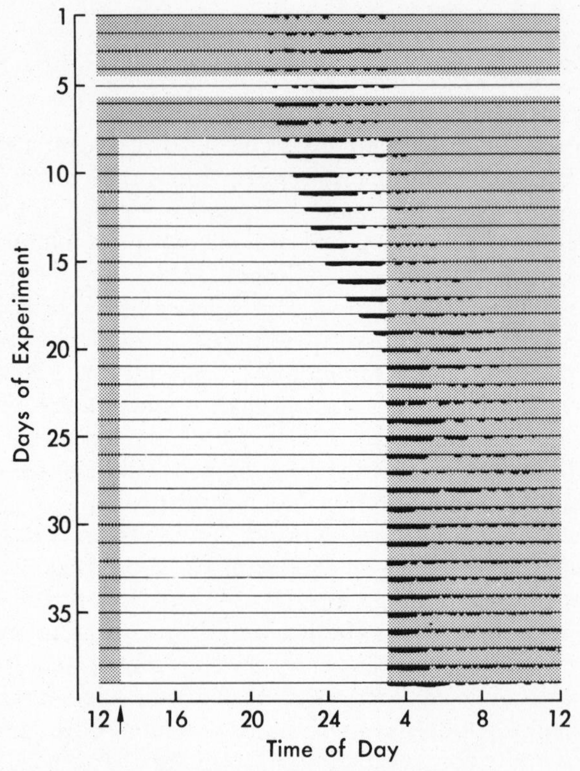

Figure 4·4. Flying squirrel changes in 12 days from one rhythm to another when the time of daylight is changed on day 8. The natural rhythm is shown when the squirrel awoke at 20 hours in constant dark (days 1–4 and 6–7) or constant light (day 5). After the light was turned on at 3 hours, the squirrel changed its rhythm. [From P. J. DeCoursey, in *Cold Spring Harbor Symposia on Quantitative Biology*, **25,** 1960.]

of physiological features coincident with hibernation. Similarly, estivation is a behavioral program to prevent the animal from getting into the extreme conditions of drought and scarcity of food. Thus, excessive demands upon the homeostatic physiological mechanisms are avoided.

Another feature of behavior important in homeostasis is the persistence of rhythms of activity in spite of temporary local disruptions.

Many species live in places where their activity depends intimately on some regular change such as tidal action or sunset. The individuals develop internal rhythms that ensure that the animal will take appropriate action such as returning to shelter or waking up even though the environmental cue is temporarily absent. For example, flying squirrels have an endogenous rhythm to wake at the appropriate time (Figure 4·4). The rhythm can be reset if the environment cue is changed. Thus, the squirrel will not respond to "false alarms" but can adjust to new situations.

In addition to behavior as a means of producing a uniform internal medium, a number of anatomical devices are used. Such things as fur and feathers are, of course, well known as protection for the animal. Another anatomical aspect, perhaps poorly recognized, is the importance of support to keep an animal away from the ground. Species that have developed the ability to raise themselves from the ground have a definite advantage in maintaining their temperature. The ground, of course, can be either hot or cold, and direct contact would result in either heat gain or heat loss. The air, since it is a moving environment, can be more easily altered in its temperature conditions. Thus, the anatomical supports found in higher vertebrates and in insects are extremely important in facilitating the development of a uniform internal condition.

Emigration. The last resort for an animal in an unfavorable environment is to get out. It may move a short distance, as the muskrat does in leaving a dried-up pond to search for another place. Or it may make a regular migration from one place to another at definite seasons, as do the big game herds of the African plains in searching for green feed. Note that movement of two types is possible. The first solves temporary, unusual emergencies that occur at odd intervals, and animals cannot develop a regular behavior pattern to handle these problems. The second solves a regular (usually annual) and hence predictable need. Animals can take advantage of regularly occurring stimuli that are correlated with the change. The best-known example is the connection between length of day and breeding of birds. Birds are not interested in longer days per se; but longer days mean (almost always) more food. The high value of the correlation between length of day and food supply means that a bird can rely on length of day. The bird has no way to measure the food supply two months in the future and a thousand miles away. But it can measure the length of day where it is and rely on the correlation. In this manner many animals have developed movement behaviors that emancipate the individual from the habitat.

Control of Environment

We have seen that throughout the evolution of animals there has been a trend toward emancipation from the habitat. The first stages of this emancipation involve behavioral patterns by which the animal either protects itself from the environment or moves to a more suitable place. Following these behavioral developments, there are physiological and, eventually, anatomical changes. Thus, behavior is the first step in the evolutionary trend. The obvious climax of a trend that passes from dependence on the environment to emancipation from the environment is the complete control of the habitat conditions. While no species, even man, has yet developed complete control of the habitat, many species have gone far in this direction. In some cases the control of the habitat is rather absolute for short periods of time or stages in the life of the animal. One simple type of habitat control is the construction of a shelter that maintains the environment relatively constant. The nests of birds and other forms offer considerable insulation for keeping the young birds warm and for maintaining their heat when the parent is off the nest. A similar function can, of course, be assigned to the use of burrows underground.

Food production is another vitally important aspect in the control of the habitat, and a number of animals have gone a long way toward producing their food supply. One of the more recent discoveries is that the reef corals, by essentially domesticating algae, have their food supply readily available. These corals are unable to exist without algae, and it appears that the algae also must be maintained by the corals. The best-known example of food production among animals other than humans is the fungus-growing ant, which cultivates a big farm of fungi to ensure its food supply. When a new colony of ants is formed, some individuals carry with them parts of the fungus so that a new fungus farm can be started. Some other kinds of ants domesticate aphids and get from them a secretion of dietary importance. Similarly, humans have gone a long way toward ensuring a constant food supply by their policies of growing domestic crops and maintaining domestic animals. The control of the food supply is a means for increasing the probability that an animal will have an adequate food supply.

A number of physiological necessities are also controlled to a large extent by behavior. For example, many rodents and other animals have developed the habit of huddling together in groups to maintain their body temperatures. Wild rats in the wintertime congregate in burrows or other locations in groups of 10 to 20 and so provide mutual warmth. The Mexican free-tailed bat lives in numbers upward of 5 million in large caves in southwestern United States. The bats spend the day in the cave and at least part of the night feeding outside. The young are born without protective fur in these nursery caves and hang on the ceiling while the female is away obtaining food. The males do not stay in the cave or tend the young, and efforts to learn their whereabouts have been fruitless. Under these circumstances, the young are essentially exposed to the environmental conditions. However, the heat produced by the 5 million bats milling around for several hours and the circulation of air in the cave creates an incubator type of atmosphere for the young bats, and their temperature is easily maintained. Here there are almost no physiological demands on the young bat. It is also well known that a similar phenomenon occurs in beehives where the temperature is maintained; the bees fan the air with their wings when the temperatures go too high. Humans have, of course, gone a long way toward emancipation from the environment by controlling first the cold conditions and now, through air conditioning, the hot conditions. Indeed, many humans can now spend most of their life where the temperature is not very different from 70°F.

The role of learning in emancipation from the environment is intricate. An animal that cannot learn, such as a protozoan, must respond to each event on the basis of actual stimuli. Avoidance of a harmful situation without direct contact is impossible; movement to a favorable situation also depends upon direct cues. In contrast, animals that can learn are able to use neutral cues to determine whether an object is useful or harmful. Consider the warning colors of caterpillars. Birds learn that certain colors and color combinations occur on caterpillars that taste bad, so instead of tasting these caterpillars each time, they avoid them, and time and effort are saved. For our purposes the type of learning is not important. However, it is essential to note that learning can be at an individual or specific level. Some things are learned within an individual's life. To illustrate, a bird known as the oyster catcher feeds on mussels. The adult birds feed the young on shucked mussels for about two to five weeks and then give them unshucked mussels. The adults then aid the youngsters in their clumsy attempts to open the mussels until the young become proficient at the task. In contrast, other things are learned on the specific level and are called innate or inherited. Hermit crabs discriminate among types of shells and without previous experience select a suitable shelter. Mite larvae of a type parasitic on dragonflies are attracted by the motions of an emerging dragonfly. Learning by any process greatly increases a species' chances for emancipation from its environment.

The conclusions from this survey of the relation of animals to their environment are that the trend is clear toward complete control of the environment. We started this study with life that was at the mercy of every little change. We saw that as time went on a number of species developed a structure that was able to protect them from the environment. However, it became obvious that such a structure was prison and must inevitably be a dead end in evolution, since the animal at some time must get out. The reason animals must get out of the structure is, of course, that with varying environmental conditions, individuals must be widely dispersed to increase the likelihood that some will be in a suitable place at all times. The alternative to the development of a structural prison is the emphasis on behaviors that allow the versatility necessary for animals to disperse and yet at the same time pursue the evolutionary trend toward control of the environment. Behavior, thus, is a major dispersal mechanism and also assists other mechanisms in their homeostatic actions. In this chapter we have seen several devices for increasing the probability that an animal finds a suitable environment. For example, animals that can control their habitat conditions have increased the probability of being in a suitable environment to 1.0 for many things. Consider humans in the United States. We have, of course, inherited the probability of 1.0 for oxygen supply. We are controlling the environment so that the probability of adequate water and adequate food are very close to 1.0. As time goes on, other conditions will have their probability increased almost to certainty.

One aspect that has evolved along with the emancipation and eventual control of the habitat has been the aggregation of animals into groups. One basic advantage of animals being close together is that the probability of fertilization of gametes is increased. In addition, such features as the construction of shelters and control of temperature are also improved when animals are together. The result of these aggregations is that animals have been forced to organize their populations according to particular systems. Several types of organization have developed and will be considered in the next chapter.

References

Hafez, E. S. E. (ed.). *The Behaviour of Domestic Animals.* London: Bailliere, Tindall & Cox, 1962. xiv + 619 pp.

Schiller, Claire H. (ed.). *Instinctive Behavior.* New York: International University Press, 1957. 328 pp.

CHAPTER

5

Organization of Populations

ANIMALS SOONER OR LATER must deal with each other and hence develop an organization: birds flock, antelope travel in herds, locusts swarm, barnacles crowd together. The simple reason for organization is that cooperation among individuals may be beneficial and thus have survival value. (The minimum connection within a sexual species is, of course, the consummation of mating.) Relations with other species develop either through competition for resources in the habitat or from the desire of one animal to feed upon another. Thus, it is extremely rare that animals live in isolation from other animals for more than a very brief period of time. Animals form a population, which we define as a group of animals belonging to the same species and having at least a minimum of organization. We usually use the term community to refer to a group of animals belonging to several different species living in the same general habitat or area. Among members of the animal kingdom occur great differences in the complexity of the organization of populations. Persistently appearing is a seasonal change in the type of organization. For example, red-winged blackbirds breeding in colonies in the spring have a territorial organization in which a male occupies a very definite area and has two or three mates. In August the young and the adults abandon their breeding areas and congregate in vast numbers in marshes, sometimes coming from many hundreds of miles. These enormous flocks then fly south and join other species in numbers in the millions. The next spring the birds migrate north and again assume the territorial behavior. An example of another sequence of seasonal changes in organization is found in woodchucks, which usually live in relative isolation. During winter they hibernate underground and in spring emerge and associate with a member of the other sex for a very short period of time. Then the sexes separate and the female raises the young, which disperse in July. For the rest of the year each woodchuck lives in almost complete isolation. Thus, the red-winged blackbird, on the one hand, lives in large flocks except for its territorial phase, whereas the woodchuck, on the other hand, lives in pairs for only a short time at mating. These two examples of seasonal change could be augmented by many more cases.

The survival values of organization are cooperative efforts (1) for defense against predators, (2) for protection in unfavorable habitats, and (3) for finding resources. Oftentimes the organization may bring animals together under circumstances that result in conflict among the individuals. On the whole, even in these situations the existence of organizations of members of the species into a group seems to have a positive survival value that enhances the production of young and the maintenance of the species. The cooperation appearing in a population is sometimes counteracted by a certain amount of disoperation, which at times may seem rather spectacular. As in so many biological situations, the net value of organization is the sum of a positive value (cooperation) and a negative value (disoperation). Those species will survive that are able to arrange their social behavior so that the selective advantage of cooperation outweighs the adverse disoperative effects inherent in the organization. This chapter will attempt to survey briefly the kinds of organizations and indicate their distribution in the kingdom.

Aggregations

An aggregation is formed when a number of animals are simultaneously present in the same place. As might be expected, these groupings of animals have little or no organization and may include several species. In such primitive animals as protozoa the members of the group may be genetically related and merely continue to exist side by side. It is usually thought that forms such as volvox, which simply remain together as an aggregation of cells after division, are prototypes of a multicellular animal. Another stage in this sequence is illustrated by hydroids, which are aggregations of cells that eventually develop a certain amount of division of labor. This chain of evolutionary events presumably resulted in the multicellular organization which, through specialization of certain parts, has great survival value. One could say that a multicellular animal is an organization of cells that have remained in direct contact and perform a variety of functions. As will be seen later, a population is an organization of animals that perform a variety of functions but the animals do not remain in direct contact. An organized population of animals has more versatility than does a multicellular animal, since the individuals do not have to maintain continuity with each other.

True aggregations of multicellular animals are found regularly under a number of different circumstances. In some cases the members remain attached together even though they show no definite cooperative effort. For example, ascidians may exist in large numbers side by side without mutual benefit but merely surviving on the same resources. Sponges also may consist of many millions of individuals living together. Another type of aggregation develops among animals of common parentage. In some cases asexual reproduction allows many hundreds of individuals to remain close together and to survive in favorable circumstances. The protozoan *Stentor* is an example of this. Other animals, through sexual reproduction, produce a large number of individuals which remain as an aggregation close to the place where the eggs were laid. Thus, aphids, tent caterpillars, and certain beetles form aggregations that are the result of reproduction. Still another type of aggregation occurs in animals that need the same resources and so feed more or less simultaneously. For example, spiders may come together and build webs in an area where, because of air currents or some special type of vegetation, insects readily may be captured. Caterpillars may thrive in large numbers where the eggs have been laid on plants that serve as food. In the tropics many birds and arboreal mammals aggregate at a tree in flower or fruit and feed there for hours. It is not uncommon to find 15 or 20 species of birds, as well as several species of mammals, during the day at one feeding place. An aggregation of this type is probably a transition phase between a group in which there is no real cooperation and a population in which various individuals benefit one another. A similar situation occurs in some fish. Many individuals congregate in a spot simply because resources are available.

FLOCKS AND GROUPS. Aggregations merge imperceptibly into organized flocks or groups consisting of members of the same species or of members of several species. From the viewpoint of behavior and survival, the distinction between unispecific and multispecific flocks is usually unimportant. Animals group together for some functional reason dealing with obtaining necessary resources. Generally some sort of benefit from the association enhances the survival value of formation of a group.

One value of grouping is based on the distribution of food. For example, a flock of grackles may cover an area systematically and by their mass effect stir up food for all the members. A recent study of cattle egrets showed that those birds that fed alongside a cow obtained food about twice as efficiently as those that fed separately. An even more remarkable example is the presence of "guests" that feed within certain ant colonies. Beetles of several different species have found that food is readily available and that other benefits occur from staying within the population of ants. A second value derived from organization into groups is protection from predators. For example, such birds as coots live during the winter on open bodies of water and when attacked by a hawk or an eagle come together in large aggregations. They flap their wings and mill about confusing the predator until he eventually gives up or picks up a straggler that was unsuccessful in joining the big group. A simpler phenomenon occurs in the aggregation of fish that, as a school, dart rapidly in different directions and presumably confuse the predators. Probably roosts of birds have survival value since mutual warning allows individuals to escape attacks. An unusual type of protective aggregation occurs in certain African birds that regularly build very close to a wasp nest. Presumably any mammalian predator would disturb the wasps and promptly leave the immediate vicinity.

Breeding brings about another type of flocking. Here the survival value apparently is the increased efficiency of finding mates. While specific mating behavior may occur, the increase in efficiency of mating is primarily obtained by aggregations in large numbers. Thus, special courtship behaviors designed to bring the two sexes together may be unnecessary. An example of this situation is found in the palolo worms, which, at time of the full moon, rise to the surface of the ocean in enormous numbers and produce eggs and sperm simultaneously. Since so many thousands of individuals are thrown together, the efficiency of breeding is extremely high. In barnacles the association of some dozen males with one female ensures that the ova are fertilized. Other examples are the swarming of mosquitoes and midges in hundreds as they mill about in courtship dances. This type of grouping guarantees copulation and fertilization both because of the mutual stimulation of the courtship and also because of the large number of individuals at a particular spot. A somewhat similar effect occurs in some mammals and birds where polygamy ensures that some production will occur, since one individual has several mates. Generally, in polygamy the male has several females, but it may also be the converse, the female having several males as mates.

A final type of flocking behavior occurs during seasonal migration. This pattern is not surprising nor unusual although it is very spectacular. Since the animals are moving in the same direction, it is natural that they would come together in groups. Presumably the group provides better opportunities for finding the way and for mutual protection against predators. The most spectacular cases, of course, are such flocks of migrating birds as geese and sandpipers. In addition, vast hordes of game mammals migrate in Africa and other areas. A dramatic invertebrate example is the monarch butterfly, which covers many hundreds of miles in flight. All of these types of groupings occur at specific times of the year and presumably confer some benefits in terms of survival of the species.

Insect Societies

The complex societies developed by ants, bees, and termites have for decades attracted the attention of students of organization and behavior. The romanticism of the early studies may have retarded the understanding of the origin and development of these social groups. First, it must be remembered that insects have had many more millions of years of time for development than have vertebrates and that some insect societies probably were highly developed at the time the first vertebrates were just emerging from the sea. Hence, one can expect many difficulties in unraveling the origin and sequence stages for the organization of insects into societies. Far more convergence in evolution can be expected, which adds to the perplexities of the investigator who is searching for phylogenetic sequences. It seems likely that the social insects developed from predaceous forms. Firstly, as we have seen in many cases, predators on the whole have highly developed sense organs and communication processes and thus were, so to speak, ready for the organization of a complex system. Secondly, many of the existing predators collect food and then lay eggs near the food. For example, a wasp digs a burrow, finds and stings a caterpillar or other large insect, and hauls the prey to the burrow. Then the wasp lays an egg beside or in the prey and when the egg hatches, the larva finds its food source readily available. Sometimes several living prey are deposited in the burrow for each egg. It is not surprising that a wasp should locate several burrows close together. Among bees occur innumerable stages in burrowing forms, from individuals that live in only one isolated burrow to groups living in burrows very close together. So, while we probably will never know the exact stages, it seems likely that the predaceous forms were ancestral to the insect societies as we now see them.

It is important to recognize that, in any group of animals, the development of a social organization rests on some basic physiological prerequisites. For the insect societies it was necessary to have several physiological conditions. One thing possibly involved was the haplodiploid sex control mechanism to permit the development of castes. A necessity was the ability of the female to absorb the ova. Connected with this is a means whereby in some manner a message can be transmitted to the female to delay the production of ripe ova. And lastly, there must be some sort of a rest or pause in development of the larvae so that periods of low temperature or of scarcity of resources can be endured without the death of every individual. Perhaps the most essential element in this set of physiological needs is the ability to cease or reduce reproduction when a crowded situation of the colony occurs. The possibilities of handling the situation seems to be inexhaustible. In some colonies excess eggs are laid but are fed to the brood and so reduce the birth rate; in others the eggs are resorbed by the female.

Division of Labor. The most remarkable development in social insects is the division of labor. During millions of years of evolution, the individuals have separated into a variety of different kinds or castes. In some species there may be a number of different castes, in others, only a few. Social insects, like most animals, have a division of labor into male and female. However, insects have elaborated the process of division of labor into workers and soldiers and even subcategories under these groups. This process has been developed in ants and termites and to a lesser extent in bees. The primitive wasps have only the primary division of labor into male and female.

It is inappropriate in a book of this type to attempt to describe the castes of any group in detail; indeed, such a description would obscure the basic behavioral importance of divisions. However, the major divisions need to be noted. An obvious separation is, of course, in terms of reproduction. The queen develops from eggs that are genetically identical with other eggs. By some process the workers select particular larvae and feed them a special diet. From these larvae develop the queens. Among ants the females not fed the special diet become workers and are sterile. The queen becomes essentially an egg-laying machine with an ovary hundreds of times as big as that of the sterile worker. Normally, there are auxiliary queens who can take over if the main queen dies. However, the colonies usually have only one or perhaps two queens actively laying eggs. The next category in division of labor is the workers. Depending on the particular insect group, they carry out the task of providing the food for the members of the colony. Bee workers bring large quantities of nectar and pollen to the hive. Ant workers bring plant food or live prey for food. The third category in the division of labor is the soldier which occurs in some ants and termites. In ants the soldiers develop from larvae that were given insect meat in their early stages; the workers develop from larvae not given meat. Termite soldiers may be either male or female. The task of the soldier ant or termite is obvious from the name, and as is well known, these individuals usually have very large pincers or stings for repelling an invader.

REPRODUCTION. The production of young is obviously an integral part of the maintenance of the colony. The spectacular queen dominates the situation and supplies eggs as long as she is in production. In ants when the queen is present, workers care for the eggs and feed the larvae at a rather slow rate. Hence, the larvae grow slowly and develop into workers or soldiers rather than into reproductive females. When the queen is absent, the larvae compete with each other for the workers' attention, and the largest ones win and eventually become queens. Thus, when the queen is present, the food is widely dispersed, resulting in large numbers of small adults rather than a few large ones. The males are generally not much modified and serve simply to fertilize the queen. Among ants the queen copulates only once and receives a supply of sperm that will last for her lifetime. In termites the female copulates many times during her life.

Reproduction among social insects may be considered at two levels. First, there is the conventional process of reproducing the insects as individuals (as just indicated), which occurs in nearly all animals. However, in addition, there is the formation of a swarm as a special type of reproductive budding in which a group of individuals bud off from the larger colony. This budding process, of course, resembles a somewhat similar operation in sponges and many of the other very primitive animals. The formation of a swarm of bees can be triggered by disturbances within the hive such as entrance of rain, smoke, or by crowding within the colony. The readiness to bud is greatest in the month of June. A minimum of 200 to 250 bees seems to be necessary. Smaller groups may swarm and start out but, unable to form a cluster, eventually return to the hive. The signal for the flight is a special "hum-dance" which precedes rather elaborate preparations. The reproductive bud or swarm contains a queen bee and a number of workers. The swarm settles on some spot and attempts to develop a new colony. This colonial type of reproduction, of course, is a new level in the maintenance of a species.

In the details of the reproduction of this vast assortment of species one can find numerous peculiarities. Species that exist have mechanisms that increase the likelihood of reproductive success. For example, some rare insect forms living in societies have several fertile females within the colony, which reduces the likelihood of extinction of the particular colony. While in most insect societies the female is fertilized by a member from outside the colony, in some of the rare species the female is fertilized by individuals within the colony, in this way also increasing the likelihood of maintenance of the group. In some termites the immature stages become sexually mature (neotenic) and are able to reproduce. This phenomenon, of course, occurs among a wide variety of animals but is still an additional method for ensuring that reproduction will be successful. Many other reproductive peculiarities could be cited.

FOOD. Provision of food by social insects has become a highly elaborate organization. Again, there are innumerable modifications, but in general the workers transport food to the colony and remove waste products. The simple, primitive case is the solitary hunting wasp, such as *Ammophila,* that carries the prey larva or insect to a place where an egg can be laid. Bees have a more elaborate system for bringing in pollen and nectar, as do the ants for bringing in live prey or vegetable food. In the tropics, where ants are so abundant, a number of species are called parasol ants because the workers cut off a section of a leaf and carry it parasol-fashion along a trail back to the colony. In many species there are elaborate processes for raising fungus on these leaves and feeding the fungus to the queen and other individuals. An important point is the sharing of the food supply among the individuals. This exchange of food has a very important function in notifying the other individuals of the sources available.

Termites have developed an additional complication by feeding upon wood. As is true in most animals, the digestive system cannot break down cellulose, and the termite must rely on protozoa for this process just as the fungus-growing ant must rely on a fungus to break down the cellulose of the leaves. However, several kinds of termites have abandoned feeding on wood and have become dependent upon fungus. To grow the fungus they have developed elaborate combs, which are made from feces and not from the chewed-up wood. The particular design and architecture of the comb are specific for individual species.

An even more elaborate organization for obtaining food is the development of slavery. One kind of ant (*Polyergus*) enslaves another kind (*Formica*) and keeps the *Formica* in bondage to provide its food. Indeed, in some cases the slavemaker population becomes relatively less than that of the slaves and is conceivably in danger of extinction.

The preceding descriptions of ant societies have necessarily been brief and have omitted intricate and diversified details for many species. The essential point, of course, is that the colony is integrated into a socially acting group. The integration occurs on a physiological level and consists of chemical messages passed from one individual to another. Food dispersed among the colony tells the kind and source available. The queen produces a substance which inhibits workers from building queen's cells and also inhibits ovarian development in the workers themselves. In addition, chemicals transmit alarms from one individual to another. However, in some cases, excited contact among the individuals gives alarm. For example, among certain termites, alarm is transmitted by contact from one larva to the others and rapidly spreads through the colony. The ultimate in integration is, of course, the control of the external environment by bees. The colony is able to contract its size during the wintertime so that the temperature can be kept at approximately 25°C when the air temperature is as low as −5°C. This temperature control is exerted in a reverse direction when, during very hot days, the members of the colony disperse and may fan their wings to cool the hive. Thus, among insects social control has developed to a very high level and has actually passed from an individual basis to a colony basis.

Organization in Space

Thus far we have discussed the organization of animals that results in some mutual benefit. However, these groupings usually bring animals together under circumstances where they compete with each other for a definite resource. The organization of populations into such groupings appears to be disoperative, resulting in negative values for survival. As will be shown here and in subsequent chapters, the organization may be disoperative for the individual concerned but actually have great value for survival of the species.

Territory

One type of organization within a population that has been intensively studied is territorial. Under particular circumstances many animals defend a definite area called a territory. This behavior occurs in a wide variety of species, including dragonflies, frogs, many fish such as trout and salmon, innumerable birds, and mammals such as seals and certain monkeys. The concept of territorial behavior was developed and elaborated by the English ornithologist Eliot Howard in a book published in 1920, *Territory in Bird Life*. Howard had studied certain buntings and warblers for many years

Figure 5·1. Australian magpie defending territory. The males use prominent perches at boundaries for song and display. [From R. Carrick, in *Proceedings of the International Ornithological Congress,* 13, 1963.]

and accumulated adequate observations to show for several species that individuals defend a particular plot of land for a considerable period of time. Other persons earlier had noticed this behavior, but none had described it exhaustively. Since Howard's time, innumerable studies, especially on birds, have shown that territorial behavior occurs in innumerable species of animals and has a number of different uses depending on the life history of the species. The variations in types of behavior are very great even within one taxonomic group such as birds. The unifying aspect of the concept is, of course, the defense of an area. This, it turns out, has survival value for the species but may not have survival value for the individual.

The following examples will indicate some of the behavior variations that occur. Since most work has been done with birds, it is natural that most of the examples will be avian. An elementary point is that the shape of the territory will depend on the habitat. Many species live in relatively homogeneous areas and thus, owing to pressure from adjacent individuals, the shape of the territory may be roughly circular. However, in some cases, as in an English bird, the yellowhammer, which lives in hedgerows, the actual territory may be long and narrow.

The duration of territorial defense depends on the life history and varies from species to species. The most common type is, of course, the maintenance of territory during the spring breeding season and

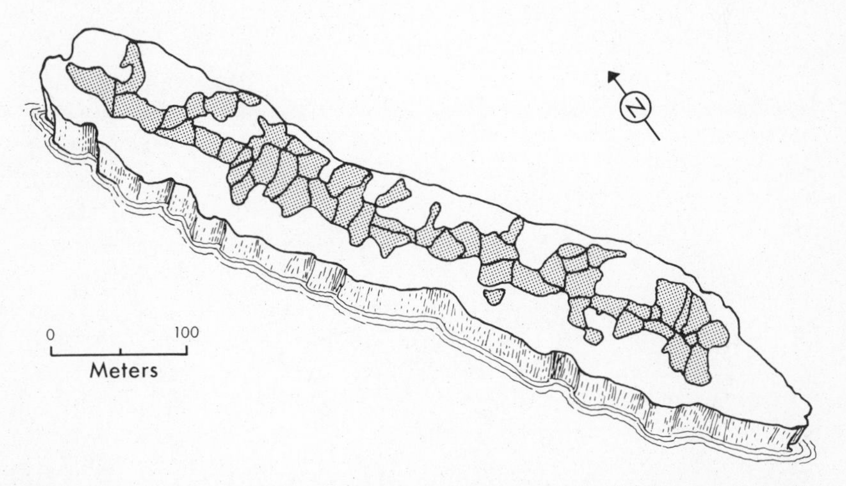

Figure 5·2. Territories of song sparrows on Mandarte Island. The size is smaller than occurs on the mainland; no additional birds could squeeze into the available habitat. [From F. S. Tompa, in *The Auk*, **79** (4), 1962.]

is illustrated by most migratory species. The classic example is the song sparrow, which arrives in the spring and defends its territory for the breeding season. Other species may begin to defend their territory in the fall. The starling, for example, in late August or September settles in the vicinity of a hole in a tree and through behavior patterns defends this spot. The male defends the hole vigorously; the female defends it rather weakly. At this time the birds are not paired. Each is merely simultaneously defending a nest hole. They maintain their activity at a reduced level during the wintertime, but if they are still present in the spring, the birds reassert their vigor and eventually may raise a brood. A number of other species that are permanent residents will also defend the territory throughout the winter. For example, the blackbird, which in England is migratory and therefore defends the territory only in the spring, is not migratory in Denmark and defends the territory from fall through the winter until the mating season. Other forms defend territory in the wintertime and then move about to select a new area in the spring. The migratory towhees select an area in their winter range and actively exclude other individuals whenever possible. The kestrel selects a suitable hunting area and drives out other kestrels if possible. Many sandpipers defend a small area around themselves during migration and in the winter. The mockingbird also defends a territory which may turn out to be the spring breeding territory. In winter, the female defends one area and the male defends another, acting as though both birds were neutral. In the spring the female ceases defense of the area and may mate with any male in the region. Some kinds of animals may defend the territory for life, especially if they are permanent residents. However, some migratory individuals come back to the same area and thus can be said to maintain it for life also. The European nutcracker spends its whole life within a small region and vigorously defends its territory, especially during the winter. It collects nuts from a rather wide area and stores them within its territory.

The size of the territory is extremely variable, depending in part on the habitat conditions and in part on the pressure of surrounding individuals. Indeed, the variation is so great that essentially no generalization can be made. It is clear that small herbivorous forms that can find a ready supply of food near the territory do not have as large an area as do wide-ranging raptorial birds. An interesting point is that some song sparrows have succeeded in nesting in Minnesota lakes on islands far smaller than the territories of song sparrows on the adjacent mainland.

A further modification of territory is its change in location as the individuals move. Partridges, especially during the wintertime, will defend an area around themselves which may be called the individual distance. The rosy finch, a bird living high in the mountains where the habitat conditions are extremely variable, will defend a territory around the female. Under these circumstances, it becomes difficult to know whether the individual is literally defending a territory or defending his mate. Another variation that might be called territorialism is the protection of the individual distance in perching birds. For example, swallows that perch on wires space themselves approximately two inches apart even though there may be thousands of birds. Similarly, starlings at a winter roost separate themselves by a small distance on a branch or on a ledge.

Territorial behavior has been studied most intensively among species in the temperate zone because most biologists live in the temperate zone. However, a number of studies recently carried out in tropical areas show that tropical birds also maintain territories. In actual practice the territories are less easily discernible, since a phenomenon in tropical areas is that in spite of the presence of many species of animals each species is represented by only a few individuals. Thus, it turns out that the biologist is rarely on hand when two individuals encounter each other. Furthermore, since the breeding season is long, there is no spectacular initiation of territorial fighting at some particular season. It has been shown that birds in equatorial forests of British Guiana defend territories when another bird invades.

Although most studies of territorial organization have concerned birds, nevertheless many other species defend an area. For example, the hermit crab defends an area and drives away, if possible, all other male crabs. Many insects defend a spot. The wasp (*Sphecius*) that kills cicadas defends a territory set up in an area where there are many emergence holes of the cicadas. The wasp threatens male wasps, other insects, and, when tricked by the investigator, even pebbles. The result is that the male has an abundant supply of cicadas for a female to lay eggs on. Another group of insects, crickets, aggressively defend a territory. Dragonflies (*Odonata*) defend territories vigorously. Evolution may have occurred in the following sequence: (1) Frequent and violent flights at any dragonfly (or insect remotely resembling one) resulted in wasted effort. (2) The development of dimorphism permitted males to identify females (and not attack) from males (and attack). (3) However, mating was inefficient if energy was used to drive males away from an area. (4) The spacing resulting from territorial defense results in increased efficiency of mating.

Innumerable species of fish defend an area. Sunfish, bass, trout, show territorial behavior in defense of a nest site. A curious modification is the defense of an area by juvenile salmon, presumably for food. Some mammals show territorial behavior, although, except for primates, the situation is confused by the difficulty of observation of primarily nocturnal species. Primates of several species defend group territories from other groups. The behavior has the same characteristics as does defense by birds.

Functions. Territorial behavior serves many functions, however, and the type of function depends upon the species. In many cases only the nest site is protected against other members of the same species. Even within this category there is great variation. For example, as Howard pointed out, birds nesting on sea cliffs defend a small territory around the nest site, so that although the individuals appear closely packed, each bird has a small territory. Other forms, such as the American goldfinch, defend an area around the nest but feed in common with other goldfinches at a considerable distance. The grebe, studied long ago by Julian Huxley, shows a somewhat compressible and variable territory. Under conditions when the nesting site and food supply are adjacent, the grebe will defend both. However, if the nest and the food are widely separated, the grebe may defend only the nest site and feed peacefully with other grebes at a distance. A recent study of the stellar jay shows still a further modification. The birds were living in an area where it was easy for the investigator to find a number of nests and to measure the defense of the territory in relation to the nest site. The vigor of defense decreased with distance from the nest. Thus, an individual dominant when adjacent to its own nest would be subordinant near the nest of another individual. Under these circumstances, the territories were not mutually exclusive but the individual nearest its nest was the top-ranking bird.

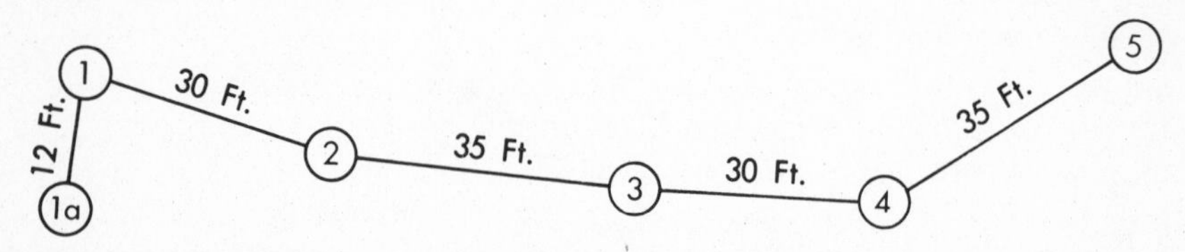

Figure 5·3. Territories in a lek of manakins. Each male maintains a station (1 to 5) by elaborate displays. Females, passing through, are inseminated. [From F. M. Chapman, in Bulletin No. 68, 1935, published by The American Museum of Natural History.]

A second function of territory is provision of a food supply, particularly in the winter. Hummingbirds illustrate this type of territorial function. The male may defend a patch of flowers that provides an excellent supply of nectar and insects. Some warblers in their tropical winter homes also defend a local area presumably in relation to the food supply. A third territorial function is the defense of a spot for courtship display. It is often assumed that a mating site was the original function of territory, although at this time it is difficult to say just what the primeval territorial function may have been. For example, a woodcock defends a particular area by elaborate displays and uses this area for courtship and copulation. The female may nest in some rather different location. Another pattern occurs in a South American bird, the manakin. The males come together in groups, each individual defending a small area adjacent to another. The females copulate as they filter through the males and nest at considerable distance. The males take no part whatsoever in raising young. In a general way this type of territorial defense occurs for many kinds of trout also.

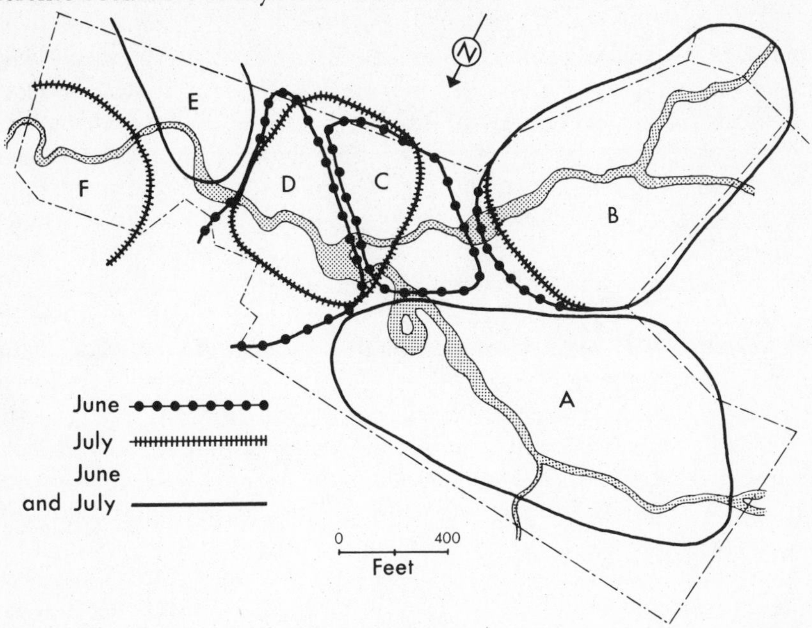

Figure 5·4. Colonial territories of smooth-billed ani. Each group (*A* to *F*) contained 5 to 15 birds of both sexes and defended a territory against other birds. In July the C group moved out and the *D* group took over. [From D. E. Davis, in *The Auk*, **57**, 1940.]

TYPES. A highly evolved type of territory is the colonial territory which is defended by a group of individuals. Curiously, this type of defense behavior has been developed in an almost identical form in groups of birds widely separated taxonomically and geographically. Several members of a genus of cuckoo in Central and South America and several Australian passerine birds have developed the ability to live together in groups of 10 to 15 individuals. The group as a whole defends the boundaries of the territory. Strange individuals find difficulty in joining the group, although they may succeed after a persistent effort of several days. The group defends the boundaries of its territory against other groups as well as against individuals.

Another modification of colonial territory is the association of individuals together in a display ground called a lek. This behavior occurs most commonly among grouse and hummingbirds. Males congregate in groups and defend a small territory serving as a place for copulation. Generally the females do not have a territory but merely pass through the area, are inseminated, and then nest at some distance.

Still another modification of territory is the development of polygamy in several species. For example, in the yellow-headed blackbirds, which live in marshes, the male defends a relatively large territory that may contain the smaller territories of several females. Red-winged blackbirds have the same type of organization. In Africa the bishop bird maintains a similar procedure except that successive females defend a territory within the territory of the male. The polygamy of the bishop bird is not simultaneous as in blackbirds, and therein lies the only difference.

Interspecific territories may involve the defense by one species against another, often closely related. For example, two species of meadowlarks, the eastern and the western, may nest close together in certain areas. In this case the territories do not overlap, but the males of each species fight against all nearby meadowlarks. In some other cases birds drive out members of almost any species. The kingbird is noted for its belligerency, driving out song sparrows, flickers, robins, and other birds intruding on the territory. Generally interspecific territorial defense is not as persistent and vigorous as the intraspecific defense.

The seeming universality of territorial behavior may have blinded researchers to the possibility that some species lack territory completely. Among birds, species such as honeyguides and the Cape weaverbirds apparently never defend a particular area. Even in certain sandpipers, the redshank for example, there seems to be no defense of a spot. This variability makes it clear that territorial behavior is not essential for the success of a species, although many forms have developed a life history sequence for which territorial defense is very efficient. Among other types of animals, territorial behavior has not been studied as extensively as in birds, and so it is rather difficult at the moment to state that territory literally is absent. However, it seems likely that many fish and invertebrates show no indication of territorial behavior.

EFFICIENCY. To maintain the territorial system a number of behavior patterns are essential. In the first place, it is necessary that the owner of a territory have the ability to recognize its neighbors. While animals might successfully defend a territory even though unable to recognize nearby individuals, the process would be extremely inefficient, for a large amount of effort would be expended in attacking individuals that have no intention of intruding. Observations of many species show that the owner attacks strangers but ignores well-known neighbors unless they intrude on the territory.

A further means of increased efficiency in defending the territory is the development of behavior patterns that reduce the necessity for actual combat. Generally the process of territorial defense in a wide variety of taxonomic groups consists first of an advertisement or notification; second, a threat; and third, if necessary, an actual fight. Thus, such widely diverse forms as dragonflies, fish, and sparrows have a similar sequence of behavior patterns. The actual mechanisms naturally differ according to the anatomical equipment of the individuals, but the behavioral meaning is clear. Through the mechanism of song, birds are able to develop a most efficient and effective manner of indicating to strangers or to neighboring individuals that that the territory is owned and will be defended by an individual. In some situations the animal may substitute for vocalizations such conspicuous structures as plumes, brilliant coloration, or may even collect substitute objects. For example, the bower birds, as has been known for centuries, collect a wide variety of curious and bright-colored objects to make an elaborate structure. It now appears that the proper interpretation of the bower is that it is an advertisement indicating that the male is defending this small area and that females are welcome. In most cases purely anatomical structures rather than cultural devices have been utilized for warning and advertisement. If notification and threat do not succeed in repelling the invader, physical combat may ensue. Under these circumstances, the two individuals fight by whatever means are available, and the vigor of the individuals determines the result. If the owner loses the fight, he will leave the area in possession of the victor. Generally speaking, however, the owner has an advantage and repels the invader. The detailed discussion of territorial behavior has occupied students of animal behavior for many years and produced voluminous literature, which will not be discussed in detail here since it is readily available in a number of books.

Some attention has been paid to the aspect of the time of pairing in relation to the time of establishment of territory, since this relation might shed light on the origin of territorial behavior. One function served by territory is to provide an exclusive and isolated spot where copulation or insemination can take place without interference from other individuals. In some cases, the male defends territory and is ready to mate before the females arrive. In this situation there is a ready-made place where copulation can occur in isolation. However, in other forms the individuals pair and together search for a suitable territory. Copulation may thus occur either before or after the territory is established. This type of behavior seems to have been first recognized among kingbirds and has later been found in a number of forms such as hawfinches and several ocean birds.

Territorial behavior has many functions for the individual and, generally speaking, increases the efficiency of reproduction. However, the behavior also has aspects important to the survival of the species rather than to that of the individual. The development of a territorial system tends to divide up the resources so that the individuals will have at least the minimum necessary for reproduction and survival. Consider the simple situation resulting from placing pigeons in a rather large cage. When one male or pair is introduced it will, of course, use the whole area and thereby have ample nesting and feeding sites. As more pairs are introduced, the individuals defend a particular spot and eventually the whole cage is divided into territories of a minimum size. Individuals added after this time cannot find a sufficient area for their needs and so do not breed. This system ensures that at least some individuals breed. In contrast, suppose that the addition of more individuals resulted in further reduction in size of the territories. Eventually a point would be reached at which there would be no breeding whatsoever, since none of the individuals had a suitably large place for finding food and for raising young. It is apparent that the division of a tract of land into territories has survival value for the species. A corollary of this proposition is that the territorial behavior may limit the density of the population. Indeed, this situation occurs in several chickadees in Europe. In these cases, the number of males is definitely determined by the number of possible territories in the area. Additional males cannot find a location and thus the population in that tract of land is restricted. The limitation of population by means of territory needs further emphasis. Field studies of this type are extremely difficult to conduct, and it is, of course, necessary to be sure that other factors are in excess so that the size of the area is the only factor involved.

Social Rank

Animals of many species have developed a means other than territory for organizing their populations. When several individuals of the same species live close together, sooner or later an order of precedence occurs in a manner that clearly demonstrates the dominance of one individual over the other. Usually the rank of the individuals is easily discerned because the subordinate animal moves away or somehow defers to the dominant individual. Generally speaking, animals that are living together have settled their social problems and do not spend much time in fighting or threatening, especially if these individuals have grown up together within a population. They know their rank and stay in their place, so no visible fighting occurs. However, one must not conclude that lack of fighting indicates a lack of organization into a rank. If the organization is somehow disturbed by removal of some individuals, introduction of strangers, or illness of an individual, fighting may result, which clearly demonstrates the ranking order.

Figure 5·5. Aggressive stance of a bull moose. Note the abnormally stiff forelegs. [From V. Geist, in *Behaviour,* **20** (3–4), 1963.]

It is not necessary here to describe the multiplicity of behavior patterns used by animals to establish rank. Suffice to say that each species has particular patterns for advertising the individual's aggressive intent and for making specific threats, which if ignored are followed by an aggressive attack. For example, mice, the best-studied species in respect to rank, initiate a contest by a peculiar posture in which the body is hunched up and the trunk foreshortened. The animal walks with very short steps. It soon begins to vibrate its tail with great rapidity often making a noise by hitting the tail against the edge of the cage. If the other mouse does not retreat, the aggressive individual will attack and fight fiercely. After a short time one individual submits and attempts to escape by running away or jumping. Occasionally the two animals fight to a draw and manage to wound each other severely. After one individual recognizes his defeat, he remains subordinate for a long period of time.

Examples of social rank are found throughout the animal kingdom. It seems certain that rank is as prevalent among the invertebrates as it is among the vertebrates, but the lack of study of invertebrates at the present time prevents citing very many examples. It has been shown that wasps demonstrate a dominance phenomenon at the entrance of their nests. A thorough study of social rank in crayfish shows that they clearly have a rank. The aggressive pattern develops early in life, and the males generally dominate the females. While the details of the actual behavior patterns naturally are different from those among vertebrates because of their different anatomical equipment, nevertheless the same sequence of advertisement and threat followed by actual fighting occurs. Crickets show a very complicated set of actions between males, some of which are certainly decisive in establishment of rank.

Social rank among various vertebrates has been demonstrated fre-

Figure 5·6. Aggressive postures of manakins. [From D. W. Snow, in *Zoologica*, 47, 1962.]

quently over the past thirty years. It is present in a wide variety of species including fish and reptiles. Dogfish, at least in captivity, show a typical organization into a rank. The smaller fish avoid the larger individuals, which are dominant. In trout, rank is clearly demonstrated when the individuals are concentrated into groups as in a fish hatchery or occasionally in streams. In certain circumstances trout defend a territory instead of having a social rank. Rank even occurs in salmon and other kinds of large fish. Among reptiles rank again is widespread. Many lizards (anoles and racerunners) clearly show the typical organization of the group into a series of ranks. As usual, the larger individuals, especially the males, tend to be at the top of the group. Rank in amphibians has not been clearly demonstrated,

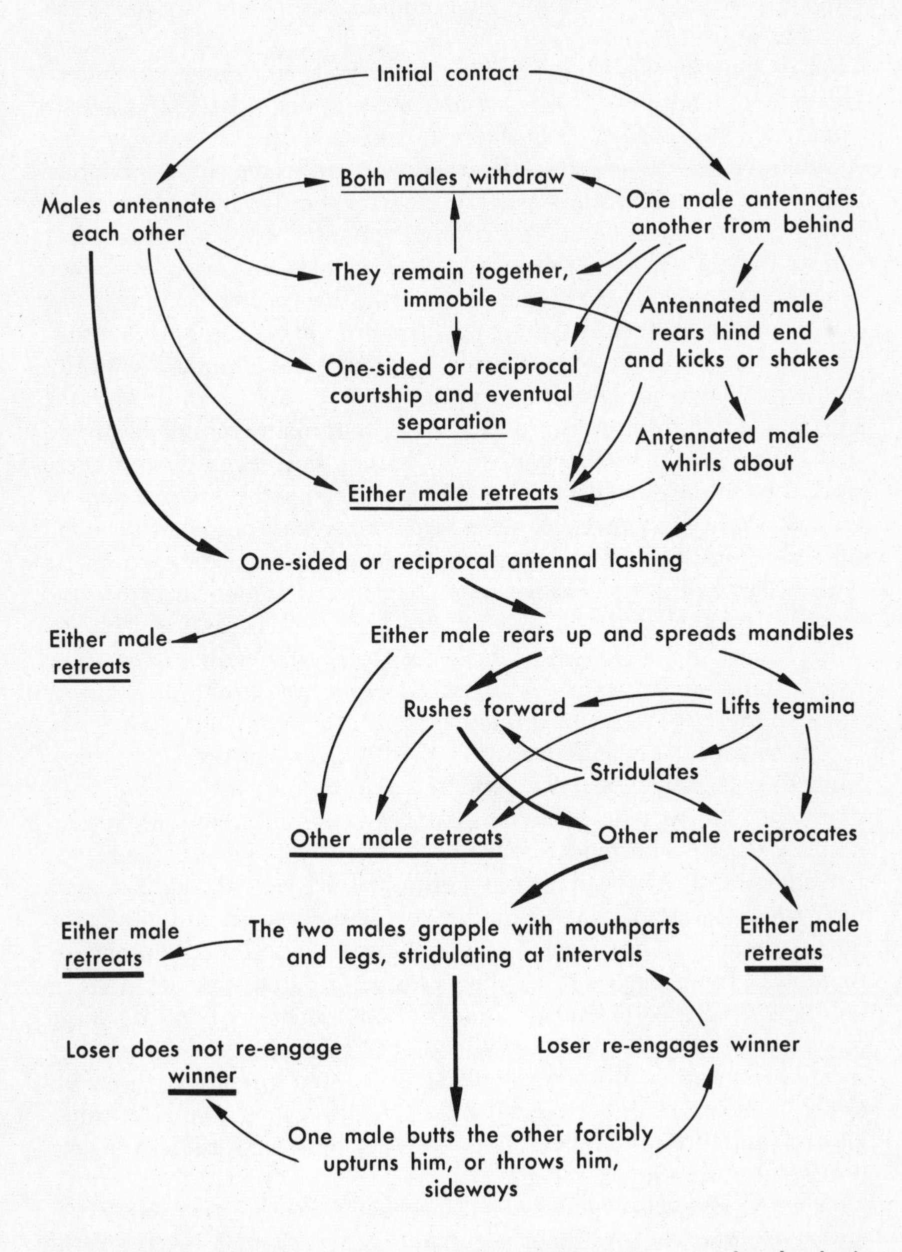

Figure 5·7. The kinds of interactions of male crickets serving to resolve the dominance relations. The combat can end at various stages as its intensity increases. Read the sequence through carefully thinking of two male crickets fighting. [From R. D. Alexander, in *Behaviour* **17** (2–3), 1961.]

probably because the proper experimental and observational situation has not yet been found.

Birds have provided the best examples of social rank, and indeed this phenomenon was first recognized among birds. In 1922 a Dutch scientist first recorded what every farmer boy knows—namely, that hens and roosters arrange themselves in an order of dominance. The situation in roosters is very clear. When four birds are put together, they soon fight and arrange themselves in a straight-line order. Usually the hens also arrange themselves in order, but when hens and roosters are together, generally the roosters will take the top places and the hens the subordinate places. Experimentally, analyses can be made of the factors influencing this rank. For example, capons are nearly always at the bottom of the rank and the injection of testosterone into either a low-ranking rooster or a hen will result in a rise in rank of at least a few levels. From these studies have developed innumerable accounts of the organization of rank in domestic as well as wild birds. However, among wild birds the manifestation of rank may not be as clear, since the encounters with others are not so easily observed. Rank is evident at a feeding tray during the winter when, for example, juncos and chickadees will arrange themselves in an order. Also, at the feeding trays some interspecific rank can be observed. Evening grosbeaks drive away other species, as just one example.

The social rank of mammals, like that of birds, has been intensively studied, especially in the domestic forms, mice and cattle. In general, of course, the specific behavior patterns must differ among species because of the anatomical differences. However, the process of advertisement, threat, and actual fighting is carried through. Cattle perform a series of threats and may actually come to blows by butting head on. This behavior is, of course, widespread among the ungulates, for it occurs in big-horned sheep, many types of African antelope and moose. Indeed, one should recognize that the large horns of ungulates are primarily for fighting for the establishment of social rank rather than for fighting against a predator. Squirrels clearly develop rank by aggressive behavior as they chase each other around and around a tree. Even camels fight aggressively in the process of setting up their rank.

Primates demonstrate rank as clearly as any mammal. Usually the group of monkeys consists of one dominant adult male with several mature females and an assortment of young individuals, who arrange themselves in an order. These animals all know their place and remain there until something happens to the dominant monkey. It is, of course, widely recognized that social rank of a variety of sorts occurs among humans. In our complicated society the ranks become rather confused because people have different ranks for different activities. For example, two people may have a rank in terms of playing tennis and a reverse rank in terms of scholastic ability. Thus, the ranking order of humans must be very closely

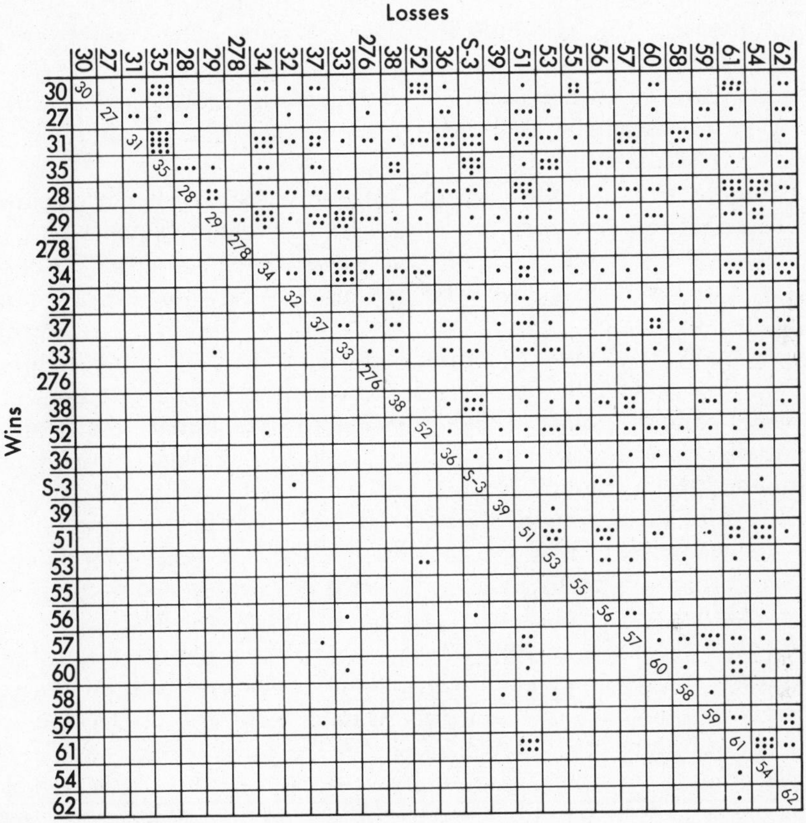

Losses

Wins

Figure 5·8. Results of encounters between cows arranged to show rank. Each cow is listed horizontally to show wins and vertically to show losses. Thus cow 29 lost to cows 28 and 35 but won over cows 278, 34, 32, etc. Some ties occur (61 and 51), and in some cases (278) rank was judged by minor actions. [From M. W. Schein and M. H. Fohrman, in *Animal Behaviour*, 3 (2), 1955.]

associated with the type of activity. In primitive societies living in less complicated situations, the rank is usually very clear and permanent and follows essentially the same sequence as the groups of monkeys.

A point of importance in connection with domestic animals is that unwitting selection by breeders has resulted in the development of nonaggressive strains. Thus, laboratory rats generally are not aggressive and do not demonstrate a rank; and some strains of white mice scarcely ever fight. These forms are not suitable, of course, for experimental work concerning the physiological repercussions of ranking behavior. Also, in nature, rank probably is far more stable than it is among domestic animals. Since the wild subordinate animal readily retreats, it has relatively little opportunity again to encounter the dominant individual. Hence, there is little opportunity for a reversal in rank. However, under domestication, mice, for example, after separation from each other for a short period of time may be put together and thereby allow for events resulting in a reversal of rank.

Numerous factors affect the rank of individuals. It is not possible to describe these in great detail but simply to mention some of the categories. Age is, of course, of basic importance. Young individuals almost always have a low rank and indeed may not even try to establish any rank. In some groups, especially in trout, the very young, called fry, develop a rank and maintain it while they are in the breeding area. It is possible that in salmon the development of a social rank is important in dispersing the individuals. Rank also may affect the growth rate of individuals. Low-ranking individuals of many species from fish to man are known to grow slowly. In part, this restriction of growth is due to the lack of food, which is taken by the dominant individuals. But in part the low rank comes from some hormonal effects. Early experience is another factor of great importance. Individuals that are early in their life placed in subordinate rank may remain there even after they mature, and other individuals not so beaten down may soon assume a high-ranking position. As a consequence of this situation the rank of the parent may be very important. For example, in the Japanese macaque, the male progeny of high-ranking mothers remain within the center of the group and soon come close to the top of the rank among the males. These individuals eventually take over the position of the dominant male. However, the progeny of low-ranking females are driven to the periphery of the group and rarely have an opportunity to take over a high rank. It appears likely that the rank is a result of basic physiological-anatomical capacities upon which is superimposed the experience that occurs during the individual's growth and development.

The results of organization into social rank are very important for the individuals. A first advantage of high rank is a mating priority. Top-ranking individuals leave more progeny, and those progeny have a better chance of success. It has been shown repeatedly for domestic fowl that the top rooster in a flock sires more chicks than do the lower-ranking individuals. Furthermore, it has been shown for primates and rats that the young born to dominant females have more rapid growth due, presumably, to a better access to the food supply. Similarly, the top-ranking individuals have a priority in finding the nesting areas which, of course, are also necessary for producing progeny. Another result of high rank is first choice of food. The dominant individual feeds first. When satiated, this individual leaves and another takes its place. Oftentimes this dominance is expressed interspecifically as well as intraspecifically. As might be expected, the value of rank is easily seen in such domesticated animals as gilts which, when crowded together, showed a clear rank at the pig trough.

TERRITORY AND RANK. The relation between territory and social rank may become very complex. Some species, under certain circumstances, maintain territories, but in other situations have a rank organization. For example, the black lizard, when at low densities, shows a clearly territorial type of distribution, although a few tyrant individuals are able to trespass on the territories of others. But when the populations become high, the system shifts to a hierarchical arrangement in which the lizards line up in a rank. This switch in organization of the population permits an increase in numbers. A similar situation occurs in canaries and in ring doves in captivity. For example, if one places two or three doves in a very large cage, each will select its territory and be dominant in that region although feeding in common in a central area. The addition of more doves will first result in more territories, but suddenly the whole territorial system collapses and the birds arrange themselves in a social order. A somewhat similar reorganization occurs in mice as their density changes.

Among birds with rather complicated breeding habits, rank may be the eventual means of organization of the population, although the initial phase is territorial. For example, many species develop a pattern of organization of a lek, as previously mentioned. The males, during the early part of the breeding season, come together into a relatively small area and there join in mutual dances or ceremonies, each restricting his activities to a small territory. In general, the birds in these areas arrange themselves in a rank, although sometimes the individuals keep separate enough so that there is no direct conflict. The females who are ready for insemination come to this area and are inseminated generally by the top-ranking individual.

The top-ranking individual usually comes into breeding activity first, and as his condition wanes, then the subordinate individuals have more opportunity for siring progeny.

Conclusions

A number of conclusions can be derived from the study of the organization of populations. First, it is clear that organization has survival value, since such a high proportion of species have become organized. Even the most primitive forms, which, relatively speaking, have no true organization, may develop some simple types of grouping. The survival value of organization occurs in two distinct areas of value to the species. The first area can be called the maintenance activities, of which feeding and avoidance of predators are examples. Grouping in flocks or schools may be of great value, since recognition of sources of food and of enemies is helpful to the survival of individuals. The second area encompasses the reproductive activities. Territories and social rank are especially useful here, but naturally survival for maintenance activities is also promoted by these last two types of organization.

Maintenance of an organization comes about through a variety of ritualized performances. Obviously, species belonging to different phyla, since they have different anatomical and physiological equipment, carry out these performances in different ways. The threats of a crayfish and of a song sparrow are anatomically very different, but behaviorally they amount to the same thing. Thus, from the invertebrates to the highest vertebrates, animals have a sequence of behavioral actions serving to indicate and enforce the organization of the population. Actually, the differences in details of these actions are not important, although very interesting; the important point is that through these actions an organization is set up. It is, of course, clear that behavior is essential in this process. The animal must first perceive that another animal is in the area and then move in some way to carry out whatever action is necessary.

Another conclusion that seems essential to understanding the organization of populations is that the development of the same organization has occurred many times within the animal kingdom. The defense of territory and the rank organization clearly are polyphyletic. Not only have vertebrates and invertebrates developed these systems many separate times, but probably a group as small as the class Aves has developed these systems independently numerous times. Clearly, there must be basic importance in such organization.

Apparently the actual details of the organization are the result of the conflict between certain beneficial effects promoting the survival of some individuals and certain detrimental effects causing death or loss of other individuals. The organization of populations is, consequently, the result of a push and pull on various characteristics in the population and thus has a basic influence on the regulation of populations.

References

Bliss, Eugene L. (ed.). *Roots of Behavior.* New York: Harper & Brothers, 1962. xi +339 pp.

Etkin, William (ed.). *Social Behavior and Organization Among Vertebrates.* Chicago: University of Chicago Press, 1964. xii + 307 pp.

Lorenz, K. Z. *King Solomon's Ring.* New York: Crowell Co., 1952. 202 pp.

Scott, John Paul. *Aggression.* Chicago: University of Chicago Press, 1958. xi + 149 pp.

Thorpe, W. H. *Learning and Instinct in Animals.* Cambridge, Mass.: Harvard University Press, 1956. 493 pp.

CHAPTER

6

Behavior and Regulation of Populations

As WE HAVE SEEN in previous chapters, behavior is the essential means for doing something about the conditions of the environment. Usually behavior applies solely to the individual animal and hence to individual survival. A new concept in biology that has attracted attention in the last decade is the role of behavior in regulating the number of animals in a population. The emphasis changes from consideration of the individual to consideration of the group, however large it may be.

The behavior of an individual consists of responses to the environment after detection of the conditions. The single-celled organisms may have fairly elaborate responses, but those of the multicellular organism naturally are far more complicated. And the responses of the population are even more complicated, especially in the problems of communication. An organism has an advantage due to connections between cells so that nerves and hormones can serve for communication; the population must develop means of communication that cross the space intervening between members. As we shall see, some old methods are put to new uses, and some new methods are developed.

An essential element in the concept is recognition that death or dispersal of some individuals may improve survival of the group and thereby be helpful in regulation of the population. Many of the social behaviors described in previous chapters are now recognized as having survival value for the population as a whole even though disastrous for the individual.

Population Regulation

The regulation of a population is strictly analogous to the regulation of an organism (through physiological processes). For example, information gleaned from the environment by an organism describes external conditions, and the organism regulates something, say temperature. Similarly, a population obtains information about the habitat, then regulates something, perhaps the birth rate.

Before discussing the role of behavior in the regulation of populations, it is necessary to remind the reader of the various means by which environmental factors limit the number of animals. A major means is exhaustion or depletion of the resources within the habitat. For example, deer may overbrowse their food supply so that not enough is left for hard times during the winter. Many examples are available of overconsumption of the food supply and some cases of literal destruction of the habitat by fouling the environment. Another means of regulation of the population is a change in the environment due to causes beyond the control of the species itself. Thus, disastrous storms, floods, or drought may from time to time occur and through destruction of food and shelter reduce the population. However, unless these catastrophes lead to local extermination, generally the population can soon return to its former level. If such events occur sufficiently frequently, the population may never become abundant but always be reduced by one or another catastrophe. However, as indicated in earlier chapters, the evolution of a species is toward improved survival in the face of environmental episodes. As we proceed up the phylogenetic scale, animals are better and better adapted to avoid or survive disasters caused by the environment. For example, animals develop devices to avoid wind or floods.

Still another means for regulation of a population is mortality produced by predators and disease, usually in combination. Under certain circumstances the predators may be sufficiently abundant to restrict the population but can only rarely exterminate it. Indeed, only a foolish predator would exterminate his own food supply and thereby commit suicide (unless he is able to travel to some other area). Again, the evolution of species has been toward an accommodation to predators so that while the predators consume a number of individuals, nevertheless the prey species is able to survive either by behavioral adaptations that permit certain individuals, usually adults, to be immune from predation or disease or simply by the device of having a very high reproductive rate. Still another means of limiting the population is the production of poisonous substances that will restrict the growth and reproduction of other individuals. Such compounds are produced by certain aquatic forms, such as tadpoles. A freshwater snail produces tricarboxylic acid in sufficient quantities to restrict growth of other snails. The chemical can be isolated and introduced into an aquarium to slow the growth. These toxins may hold down the population within the capacity of the environment to supply food and shelter.

Homeostatic Regulation

The aforementioned means generally are beyond the control of the members of the species. It is true that depletion of the habitat might conceivably be avoided if the members of the species could agree upon a level of consumption, but even among humans it is extremely difficult, for example, to persuade cattlemen to restrict the number of animals per acre. Also predation has some elements of self-regulation, but, generally speaking, these means cannot be controlled by the members of the prey population. In contrast, other mechanisms are essentially homeostatic but on the population level rather than on the individual level. It is desirable to review for a moment the characteristics of homeostatic mechanisms. It will be remembered that this concept was first proposed for the regulation of the internal environment of the mammal and was later extended to other species. The essence of the idea is that the body contains a large number of interacting and opposing physiological processes that prevent extreme changes in the temperature, blood composition, and other features. To illustrate, if the temperature rises, a number of processes that tend to reduce the temperature come into play. It is important to recognize that the condition (for example, temperature) is never constant but fluctuates narrowly around a mean. Also, lags may accentuate the fluctuation so that rarely does the condition settle down to a steady optimum level; on the contrary, it fluctuates up and down, since the lags can never exactly compensate. For the regulation of the various conditions it is necessary that a feedback mechanism be negative—that is, act counter to the change. In contrast, a positive feedback would accentuate the change and result in a catastrophe.

Recently it has been recognized that such homeostatic self-regulatory mechanisms occur in populations and keep population fluctuations within limits. The various mechanisms for regulation of a population are far more elaborate than for regulation of some physiological conditions, since they include not only a physiological aspect but also ecological and behavioral features. Indeed, behavior is the essential means of communication of data about the environmental conditions to the individual and thereby plays a key role in initiating feedbacks. Thus far homeostatic feedback mechanisms for populations have been studied intensively only among the vertebrates. Presumably mechanisms occur in various invertebrates, such as grasshoppers, but perhaps only vertebrates have attained the necessary degree of emancipation from the habitat. Among vertebrates there are many possible systems, but as will be seen, only one has been explored in detail. It is essential to recognize that in the future other systems will be discovered among the vertebrates, and some will be recognized among the invertebrates.

Population Forces. For an understanding of the current knowledge of a population feedback mechanism, we will need briefly to consider what are called population forces. These forces are essentially push and pull processes that can either increase or decrease the population according to their relative magnitude. The first of these forces can be called natality or reproduction. It clearly is a means of increasing the population and can vary with the level of population. It, of course, has an upper limit in the physiological capacity of the species to produce young. The second force is called mortality and refers to the death rate of the members of the populations. Mortality rates may be high or low, depending on the circumstances, and have great range of variability. The third force may be called migrality or movement and refers to the immigration or emigration of individuals with respect to the population. Again, this force varies greatly according to the circumstances and can be high or low in response to external conditions.

Feedback Mechanism. To discuss the one behavioral feedback mechanism that has been studied in detail, it will be necessary to digress into anatomy and physiology to provide an adequate background. Recent studies have demonstrated that a number of external circumstances will activate the region of the brain known as the hypothalamus, which in turn stimulates the pituitary. Some of the environmental conditions are toxins, infections, and wounds, but the most important aspect, from our viewpoint, is that aggressive behavior can initiate the sequence of events. It has been shown clearly for several mammals and some birds that the competition that goes on in the organization of the social rank results in numerous physiological changes. Thus far this phenomenon has not been shown to occur in territorial species, but we can be sure that the behavior of defense of territory, if adequately studied, would illustrate the same phenomenon. Now it is necessary to consider anatomy and endocrinology to show how the behavior eventually affects the population. The stimuli coming to the hypothalamus cause the pituitary to release a number of hormones that affect other organs. For our purposes, the most important hormone is adrenocorticotropin (ACTH), which stimulates the outer part (cortex) of the adrenal gland. This part is divided into several layers, but the important point to note here is that this cortex produces hormones of many sorts called corticoids. Among the effects of ACTH and corticoids is inhibition of the gonads and, consequently, accessory reproductive organs. Also there is interference with the production of protein. The significance of these effects will appear later. The gonads, of course, are the ovaries and testes, which through secretions of hormones, control the size of accessory ducts and glands.

For the study of behavioral feedback mechanisms, mice of several domestic strains, as well as other rodents, such as field voles, woodchucks, and rats, have been used. The routine procedure is to put a group of individuals together, observe the social rank, and follow various physiological measures of reproduction and of mortality. In some cases the group consists of members of one sex placed together for a few hours a day; in other cases, a large population is derived from the breeding of a few individuals in a large cage. While these techniques differ considerably, in actual practice they lead to similar results. A decade ago, when this topic was first studied, it was found that the adrenals of wild mice put together in groups were larger than the adrenals of mice kept in isolation. For example, in a recent experiment the adrenals of mice exposed to other mice averaged 5.67 mg, while those of mice not exposed to others averaged 3.56 mg. As biochemical techniques developed it became clear that even before an increase in size of adrenals became measurable, an increase in the production of corticoids occurred. It was also shown that the size of the adrenals was inversely related to the social rank: the lowest ranking mice in a group had the largest adrenals. Indeed, the adrenals of the top-ranking mice were essentially the same size as the adrenals of the isolated individuals (Figure 6·1). Numerous other studies of mice in groups have shown in detail that a decrease in activity of the gonads, usually as measured by the size of the accessory organs, occurs and that there may be some interference with the process of lactation as well as of pregnancy. A different phenomenon is the effect on the metabolism of proteins which results in a decrease in the thymus and a change in resistance to infections. This change in resistance comes about in at least two ways: (1) an alteration in the inflammatory processes and (2) a lower number of antibodies in the blood. The net result of this long chain of complicated processes is that the reproductive rate is generally lowered and the mortality rate is increased as a population increases.

These changes naturally tend to regulate a population. Consider a situation where a small number of individuals start a population, perhaps mice that have recently colonized an island. At first the

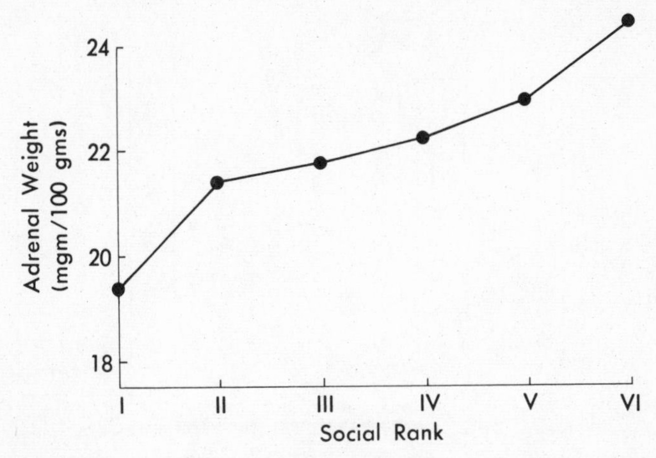

Figure 6·1. Relation of adrenal weight to rank. The dominant mice had adrenals about the same size as isolated individuals; the subordinate mice had larger glands.

growth in numbers is rather slow because the animals need time to learn their way around and may have difficulty in finding another individual. Subsequently, the rate of increase becomes high because the animals are sufficiently abundant to find each other easily and yet not too abundant to interfere with each other or to deplete the food supply. However, as the population increases, the frequency of interactions increases, aggression becomes more frequent, and the long chain of physiological events starting with the hypothalamus begins to exert its effect. At first the effect may be trivial and essentially impossible to detect, but as the population increases, the behavioral aspects attain a greater importance. The result of these events is that the natality rate decreases. There may be an increase in the age at sexual maturity or at first parturition, which, of course, slows down the reproductive rate. The number of young may also decline because of resorption of embryos, and furthermore, there may be a greater time interval between pregnancies. The net result of all of these factors is a gradual slowing down of the reproduction. Conversely, the mortality increases beginning within the uterus and continuing at birth and during the immature stages. At low populations the survival of the young individuals just after weaning is

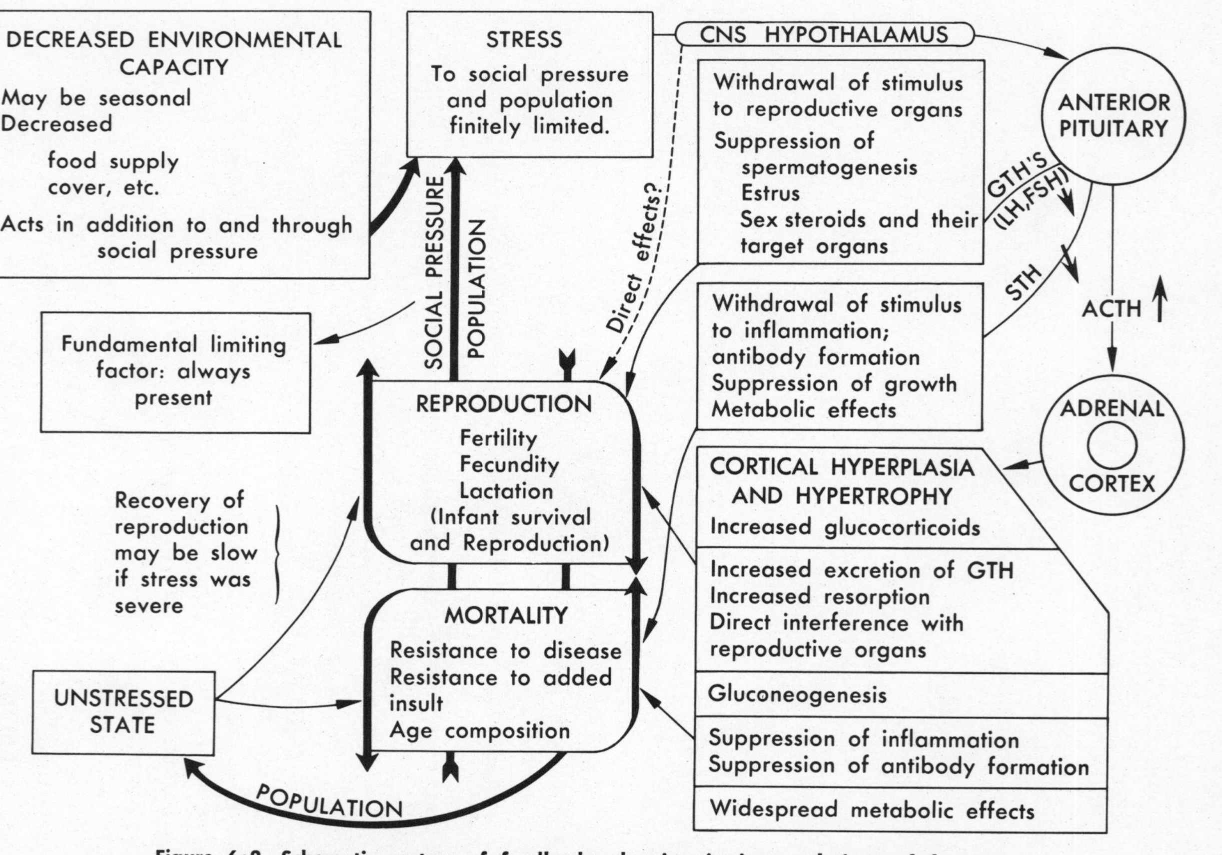

Figure 6·2. Schematic system of feedbacks showing intricate relations of factors influencing birth and death rates. Not all relations are shown and recent data suggest a few modifications. [From J. J. Christian, *Wildlife Disease*, 1959.]

very high, but at high populations the survival is very poor. Mortality of adults changes little during an increase in population but remains more or less constant. Sequences such as this are hard to document in nature, but a laboratory model (Figure 6·3) shows the history of a population of mice in a large cage.

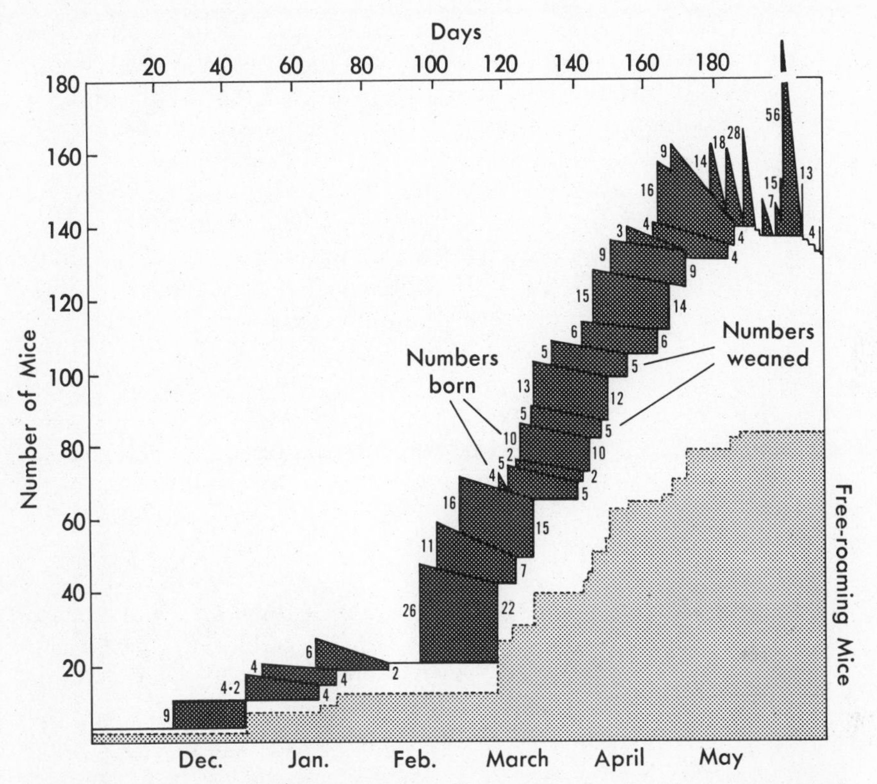

Figure 6·3. Increase in mice living in a cage. The figures on the left of each hatched block represent the number of mice born; the numbers on the right, the number weaned. Note the great increase in nursling mortality at higher densities. [From J. J. Christian, *Proceedings of the National Academy of Sciences*, **47** (4), 1961.]

Reproductive Behavior

In the regulation of a population the behavioral aspects of reproduction assume a dominant role. From the preceding discussion of population forces it is clear that when no animals enter or leave a population and the birth and death rates are equal, then the population will remain stationary—that is, be regulated. Animals cannot alter the mortality rate significantly through their behavior. It is true, of course, that animals can learn to avoid predators and to stay away from areas that are dangerous. However, generally speaking the behavioral possibilities for altering the mortality rate are extremely small. In contrast, the behavioral actions affecting the birth rate are very great and merit considerable discussion in this chapter. Animals, through a variety of behavioral patterns, differing according to the species, increase the likelihood of meeting and of successful fertilization. These behavioral patterns serve first to get the individuals together and then to synchronize the activities of the reproductive organs so that eggs and sperm are simultaneously produced.

The important aspect from the viewpoint of reproduction is that this elaborate sequence can be easily interrupted or deranged by changes in the sequence brought about by some external stimulus. Thus, the birth rate is very susceptible to modification in contrast to the death rate. At least in vertebrates the sequence of reproductive processes is very long, permitting modification at various stages and thereby allowing greater precision in modifying the rate. Consider birds, for example. There are opportunities for variation in the age at first breeding, the interval between clutches, and the number of second or third broods. All these aspects are controlled by behavior, and thus behavior has a regulatory action on the birth rate, allowing for flexibility from year to year or place to place.

The sequence of reproductive behaviors is functionally similar in all animals, although the complexity may vary. The first problem is identification. Marine animals usually identify the sex by a simple chemical test, possible in an aqueous environment. Terrestrial and some marine species use actions as well. Remember that the first thing to determine is whether the other animal is friend or foe or neutral. In a sense animals do not need to know if another individual belongs to the same species; the significant point is whether it fights, mates, or runs away. Consider the case of a rooster in a yard with several other fowl of various species. As the rooster walks about most individuals avoid him; an occasional rooster may fight briefly; a hen may squat after a little persuasion by the rooster. Behavior thus is the mechanism for identifying the reproductive individuals in the population.

Among the lower invertebrates, especially marine, the courtship behaviors primarily involve extensive movement so that the members of each sex come together. In many cases this problem is solved by hermaphroditism; in others such formidable numbers of gametes are produced that some get together without any behaviorial assistance.

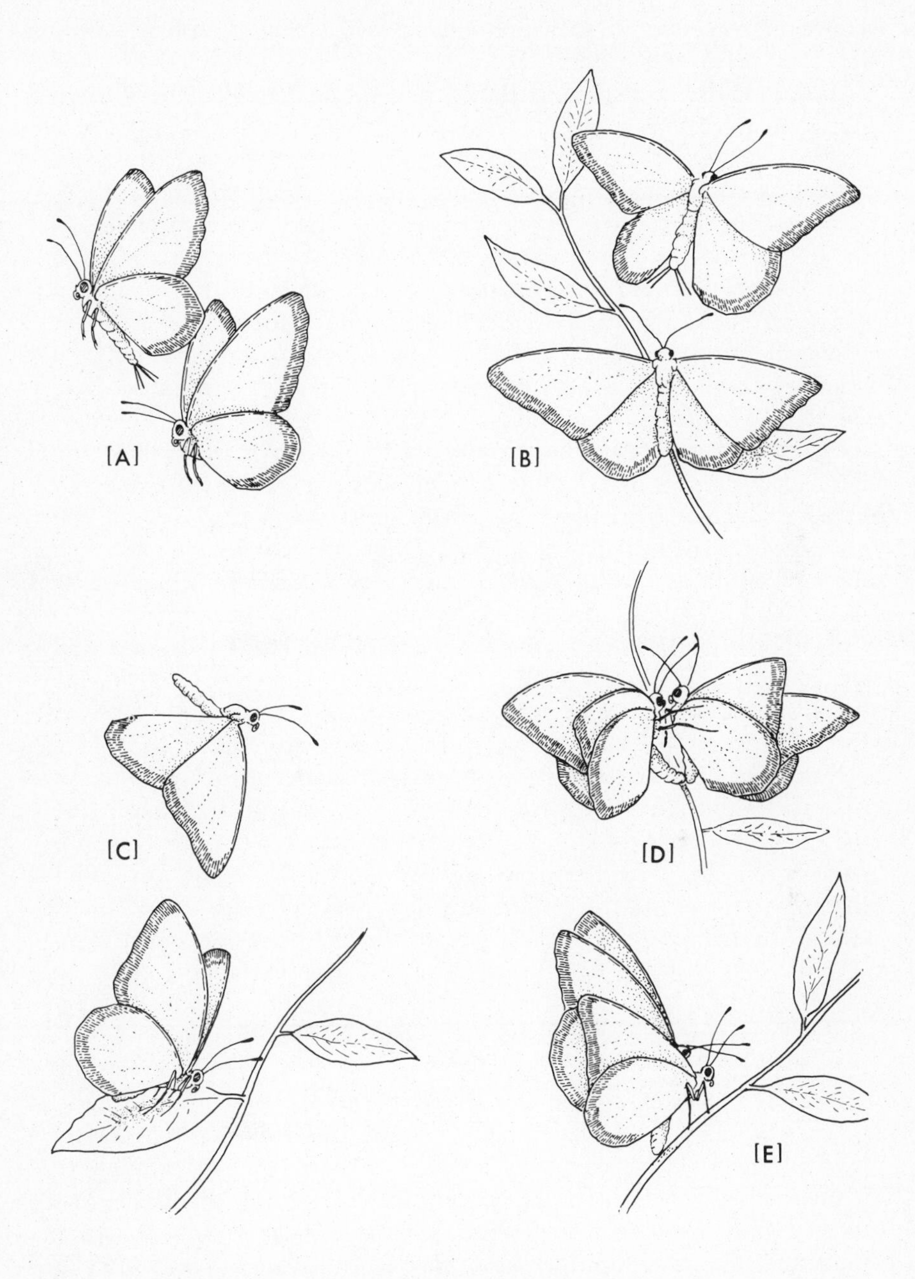

Figure 6·4. Courtship performance of Queen butterfly. A: The male is above the female with hairs on end of abdomen spread. **B**: The female has perched and the hairs are spread further. **C**: The male hovers above the female before descending (**D**) to copulate and (**E**) to palpate the female's antennae. [From L. P. Brower, in *Zoologica*, **50** (1), 1965.]

However, some species such as squids have elaborate patterns rivaling those of vertebrates in complexity.

Insects in many cases have elaborate courtship performances, often using chemicals as attractants to bring the sexes together from a distance. Some butterflies (Figure 6·4) perform a courtship flight almost as elaborate as that found in birds or mammals. First, there is a meeting of the two sexes which may be facilitated through the diffusion of some chemicals (Figure 6·4*A*). At this time the male approaches the female, spreading certain hairs on its abdomen (Figure 6·4*B*). Then follows the flight in which the male may hover above the female (Figure 6·4*C*), presumably stimulating her reproductive organs. Eventually, contact and copulation take place after the female has alighted on some branch (Figure 6·4*D, E*). This performance requires several minutes and apparently stimulates the nervous system of the female as well as of the male to bring the gametes into parts of the body where fertilization can occur. Such elaborate courtship performances have not frequently been described for invertebrates but presumably are very common, being simply neglected in the zoologist's preoccupation with vertebrates.

In fish the patterns vary from the simplest extrusion of eggs and sperm into the ocean in some of the commercially important marine fish to elaborate chases performed by many freshwater fish. Consider the darters, small fish that live in rocky, slow streams. Their name comes from their habit of darting out from under a rock to attempt to corral a female. The male in the breeding season first cleans the underside of a big rock and then perches there. When another fish comes along the male darts out and attempts to drive the fish under the rock. Only a receptive female will respond. Under the rock the two settle side by side using various body and fin motions for mutual stimulation until the female begins to lay eggs, attaching them to the cleaned surface of the rock. The male emits sperm simultaneously. This basic pattern is found in at least 14 species, but the details of courtship differ. The angle between the two fish while settling under the rock varies from completely parallel stance, both upright, to various degrees of slant and eventually parallel but the female upside down. These slight differences in courtship are enough to identify members of the same species, so that mating occurs in most cases within the species and no gametes are wasted. Note that this sequence can go wrong in many places, resulting in a reduction of birth rate. As we shall see later on, hormones are essential for perfection in courtship behavior and can easily be deranged at least in the few species studied carefully.

Among amphibians the courtship behavior is still relatively simple as exemplified in the frog often seen in the laboratory. The female comes near the male presumably in response to his croaking. The male grabs the female with a very strong clasping reflex and holds her while she extrudes the eggs, which are fertilized by sperm from the male.

Among reptiles the courtship behaviors are still rather simple, although the individuals must come into connection for internal fertilization. Thus, more elaborate behavior patterns are involved in the courtship of snakes and lizards.

Among birds courtship behavior has developed to a fantastic level of elaborateness producing complete synchronization. An important trend occurs in that the more primitive species such as penguins, loons, and herons have very elaborate ceremonies, whereas the more advanced species such as thrushes and sparrows have less elaborate ceremonies. Why this relationship should occur is a puzzle. At any rate in birds many examples of courtship performances are available. Long ago the courtship of grebes was described. Depending on the species, it involves an elaborate sequence of swimming, head jerking, and eventually a mutual swimming performance in which the birds rise off the water, standing on their tails so to speak. Another type of display performed by such diverse birds as quail and wrens is the antiphonal singing back and forth between male and female. This behavior occurs in dense jungles of the tropics where possibly visual synchronization is difficult and hence the vocal means is necessary. In some species the singing occurs at night, whereas in others it occurs during the daytime. Numerous other examples could be cited to illustrate the point that display occurs in elaborate forms in a wide variety of birds.

For mammals display is by no means as elaborate but perhaps is equally important. In the large number of mammals that are nocturnal in habit, visual actions are less important than are chemical or tactile means of synchronization. The behavior of some primates involves mutual preening, licking, and even a type of kissing as part of courtship. Many members of the deer tribe have a sequence of vocalizations followed by nudges which eventually stimulate the female to stand for the male.

FUNCTION. It is not the purpose of this chapter to give an exhaustive review of courtship behavior but simply to indicate a few of the patterns so that a discussion may be developed concerning the function of courtship behavior in regulation of populations. For this purpose it is necessary to consider some of the available knowledge concerning the role of hormones in courtship behavior. Unfortunately, information is both meager and confused, so that a clear story cannot yet be given. However, the outlines, at least of future research, are rather clear. For many animals the male hormone testosterone is known to control the courtship behavior. This conclusion is best shown in the conventional story of the rooster. The capon shows no interest in the female, but when injected with testosterone will soon begin courtship behaviors and eventually go through with a complete performance. In the female estrogens have been shown to cause females to become receptive. Superimposed on these endocrine factors is the development of learning. Indeed a

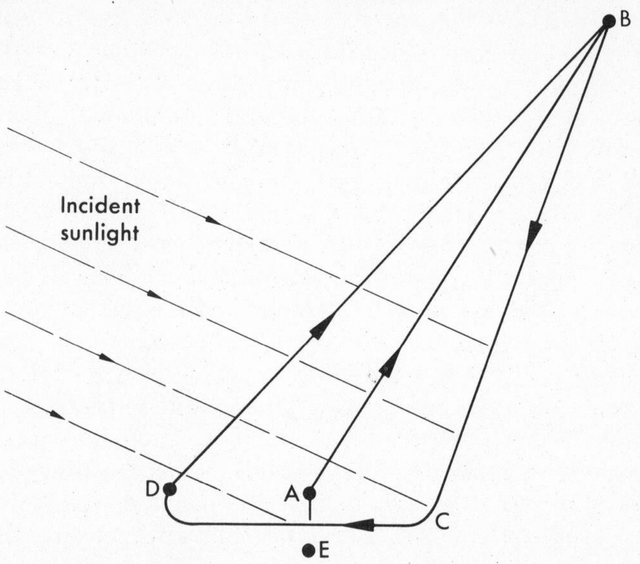

Figure 6·5. Sun-oriented display of the Anna's Hummingbird. The male hummer starts at *A* above the object *E* (usually a female), rises to *B*, hovers and dives to *C*, *D*, oriented into the sun. The hummer rises to *B* again and repeats the dive several times. [From W. J. Hamilton, in *Wilson Bulletin*, *77*, 1965.]

mature rooster will attain courtship behavior on a relatively low level of hormone in contrast to a young animal. Work done with some mammals suggests more or less the same relationship, but little is known for lower vertebrates and invertebrates.

The importance of this hormonal connection is that as the population increases, the feedback mechanism previously indicated begins to act upon the pituitary, which in turn affects the gonads. The story is at the present time incompletely described, but at least some of the effects are clear. For example, the ACTH produced by the pituitary in greater amounts at times of high populations and frequent social interaction has major effects on the adrenals. These in turn may affect at least certain aspects of the reproductive organs. However, the ACTH also directly affects the ovaries, at least of female mice, causing a delay in maturation. Thus, for example, house mice may reach sexual maturity at the age of three months when kept in isolation but may not reach maturity until six months in a crowded population. This action of ACTH affects behavior indirectly through its influence on the production of hormones from the gonads. It has been shown clearly from work on injection of hormones or on the behavior of intersexual fowl that animals with low levels of hormones show incomplete courtship behavior. Thus, the story is completed in a general outline between the increase and regulation of a population and the behavior of animals in relation to courtship.

Behavior is affected generally by low doses of hormones in a short time. Thus, it is more sensitive than an anatomical character to slight decreases of hormones. Consider intersexual roosters—genetical males so altered in embryo that they are partly feminized. Some individuals had a plumage that was completely masculine, but their courtship behavior was weak and their small comb indicated a slight deficiency of male hormone. The relevance to population regulation is that small decreases in reproductive hormones brought about at high populations may reduce the courtship behavior and thus the birth rate long before any obvious anatomical changes occur in the sex organs. In this manner behavior is a very sensitive measure of population density.

PARENTAL CARE. The preceding discussion has been concerned with the courtship behavior of adult animals leading to production of young. In addition, of course, behavior is involved in the care and maintenance of young, which is an essential aspect in the integration of the family. As was true for courtship behavior there are many descriptions of the care of young by their parents. In primitive invertebrates the young need no care whatsoever, since the eggs and sperm meet in the aqueous environment and the parents are far away. However, in a number of forms there are devices for protecting the eggs by enclosing them either within the body or within a capsule of some sort. Insects, of course, have elaborate means for protecting their eggs, usually not by the adult itself but by some structure. The tents of caterpillars are a familiar example. The ultimate complexity among insects is, of course, the care of the young by bees and wasps.

Among vertebrates one again can cite innumerable examples ranging from the most casual neglect by some of the commercially important marine fish to such bizarre performances as keeping the young in the mouth of the male while they are developing. Maintenance of a nest site and a kind of incubation are common among fish. Many species such as bass or trout scrape out an area on the bottom, allowing a depression to form for the reception of eggs. Others may defend the eggs and site for a period of time. Among amphibians and reptiles several variations occur in the care of the young. Many, such as frogs, essentially ignore their progeny, but others, such as some snakes, are viviparous and carry the young within the body until hatching. The adults may protect the young through an incubation period or may let them wander freely.

As is well known, birds regularly devote much energy to the protection and maintenance of the young. The eggs are incubated by one or both sexes, in some cases developing rather elaborate exchange performances. Some species, such as penguins, exchange sexes on the nest after a period of a month or two, accompanying this exchange with a fantastic performance or greeting ceremony consisting of elaborate bows and vocalizations. Other species, such as our common backyard birds, exchange incubation at intervals of ten to 30 minutes, nevertheless, using a very modest form of greeting. Behavior does perform an essential element in incubation by serving to control the exchange of adults at the nest. A similar situation occurs in connection with the supply of food to the young.

Among mammals maternal behavior is developed to an important extent, although its need is greatly reduced in the early stages of growth by the mechanisms of pregnancy. Nevertheless, suckling and care of the young are vital for adequate socialization and development.

Population regulation is maintained in part through effects on the care of the young acting, at least in a few cases, through hormones. While very little research has been conducted on this topic, it is clear that in some way at high populations maternal care of young mice is deficient. How much is strictly behavior (licking, suckling, warming, retrieving) and how much is physiological (quantity or quality of milk) remains to be discovered. For our purposes it is only necessary to note that behavior plays a delicate role in altering the birth rate at least a little. And when one is dealing with rates in a large area for several years, a little change can result in big differences in numbers.

To summarize this section on courtship and maternal behavior it may be noted that elaborate behavior patterns occur which can easily go wrong due to their enormous complexity. Slight variations in the physiological control of these patterns may disrupt them enough so that breeding and the birth rate decline. These disruptions can occur as a result of ecological factors (cold, drought, and so on) but also as a result of behavioral competition with other members of the same species. Thus, aggressive behavior at high populations has the opportunity to affect courtship and maternal behavior adversely, thereby reducing the birth rate. The alterations in behavior need not be great; slight aberrations of the complex system will reduce the production of young.

Perspective

The behavioral feedback mechanism has been studied in great detail as indicated in the references. For our purposes, the emphasis should be placed on the behavioral factors and on the perspective that one currently must take on the importance of a negative feedback mechanism. It is first necessary to emphasize that we are concerned with the effect of increased aggressive behavior among individuals as the population increases. Behavior patterns serve to restrict the growth of the population, so that it is held within the capacity of the environment and thereby the population is maintained at a somewhat constant level. Behavior is the unifying process of communication which essentially informs other animals about the situation in terms of population density. The action resulting from communication occurs through a number of different mechanisms. One extremely important mechanism is the movement of individual animals. A young or subordinate individual, encountering an aggressive, well-situated adult, generally will move out of the area, thereby reducing the number in the population. Thus movement (emigration) is the initial mechanism to regulate the population. In some cases it may suffice and no other mechanism may be needed. The movements of male woodchucks (Figure 6·6) can be compared in a dense population (control) and in a sparse population (experimental). Note that in the dense population the home range of adults was restricted and that both yearlings and young traveled long distances, presumably leaving the area. In contrast, in the sparse population the adults had larger home ranges, and fewer yearlings and young traveled.

Another behavior mechanism discovered very recently is physiological and may reduce the birth rate. The odors from a strange male somehow derange the reproductive hormones of a recently inseminated female. When a strange male meets a recently inseminated female some hormonal process is disturbed so that, in many cases, the blastocysts fail to implant, and thus the female will not become pregnant. Thus far, this mechanism has been recognized in only two species of mice in the laboratory and has only theoretical importance for regulating populations. However, its importance to us is for perspective on various feedback mechanisms, helping us to realize that many types of physiological mechanisms may exist and remain to be discovered in the future. At present the only mechanism that has been adequately studied is the pituitary-adrenal as previously

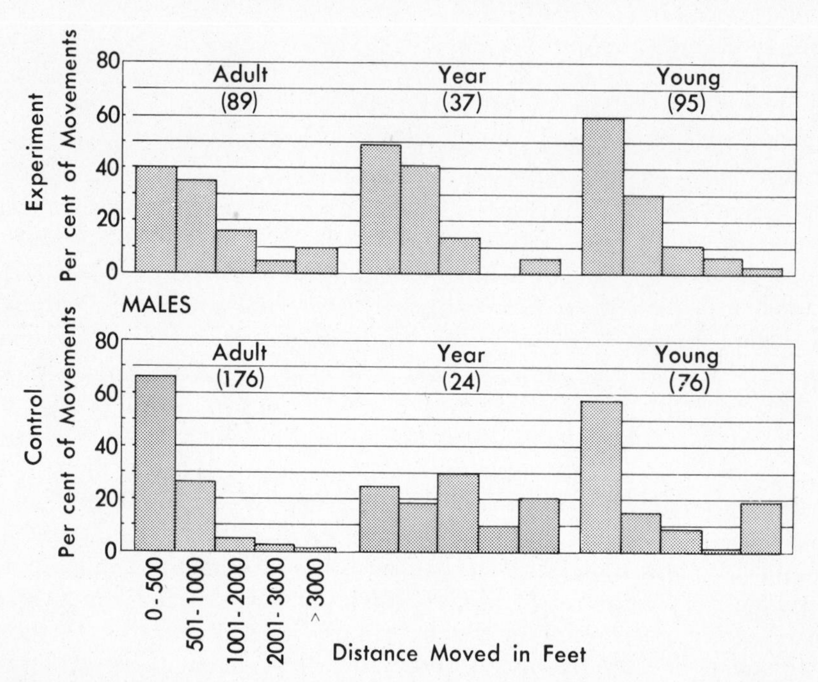

Figure 6·6. Recapture distances of woodchucks in area with few adults (experiment) and many adults (control). Note the greater home range of adult males in experimental area, and the dispersion of yearlings and young in the control area.

described very sketchily. There is no doubt that in many cases this mechanism comes into play and holds down the populations. The actual extent of application of this mechanism to vertebrate populations remains to be determined. Certainly it will be found to be common among mammals, birds, and perhaps even fish. However, in some species other mechanisms are known. For example, fish produce metabolic products that are toxic and restrict the growth of other individuals.

The important point is that behavior through various mechanisms can restrict population growth. For an understanding of the regulation of populations, it is necessary to search for various types of mechanisms and to determine what species have mechanisms. For example, it is clear that mammals and some other vertebrates have feedback mechanisms, but it is not known whether insects have feedback mechanisms. However, the desert locust may demonstrate a physiological mechanism. Locusts increase the level of their activity as the density increases, and eventually the actions of the nymphs inhibit the maturation of the immature males, thus reducing the reproductive rate. However, the existence of feedback mechanisms is not necessary for behavioral regulation of populations; it is only an additional attribute. Even among vertebrates, direct mortality (which has no feedback) within a species may occasionally occur, and movement (emigration) regularly occurs. Among insects behavior as manifested in competition often limits the population, but as yet no feedbacks have been recognized. Generally some ectocrine (external hormone) is effective. For example, a triclad worm produces a substance (as yet not identified) that reduces the number of cocoons and increases the age at time of production. Thus, the number of cocoons is inversely related to the number of worms. Presumably many species produce such substances.

Efficiency

Finally, the significance of bluffs and threats needs recognition. Innumerable ethological and life history studies have described the patterns of threats by fish (Figure 6·7), lizards, song sparrows, and

Figure 6·7. Fighting postures of two male sunfish. Note that the positions are unusual and could not be confused with normal swimming motions. [From J. R. Hunter, in *Zoologica*, **48**, 1964.]

mice. The common anole lizard sold in pet stores as a chameleon performs a definite sequence of behavior patterns when a stranger approaches. The owner of the territory raises its head and flashes its throat skin (dewlap), which becomes a brilliant blue color. Usually the threat suffices, but if the stranger persists a "mouth-to-mouth" fight occurs. Such behaviors describe to other individuals the population situation in time to prevent an encounter that might be disastrous for both individuals. From the viewpoint of maintaining a species it is better to use a warning threat to drive a competitor away than to waste energy in fighting.

The significance of behavior in the regulation of population size should be considered from the viewpoint of energy. Evolution, as pointed out in 1925 by Lotka, consists largely of increasing efficiency in use of energy. Let us consider two hypothetical cases, one inefficient and the other efficient. Suppose that a species produces many progeny with no consideration of the habitat conditions. These young may grow if conditions are temporarily favorable but may later die in large numbers owing to some catastrophe or to depletion of resources. The wastage of energy is enormous. In contrast, another species may produce progeny in numbers large or small depending upon habitat conditions. After the young are produced, if changes in the habitat occur, infant or juvenile survival also adjusts to the habitat conditions. Under these circumstances the efficiency of use of energy is high.

Behavior provides the communication system necessary to increase efficiency. Behavior by means of threats first indicates the number of animals in an area so that intruders are distributed efficiently throughout their range. If the population is dense, intruders leave; if it is sparse, intruders stay because they are not threatened. However, higher animals do not rely completely on movement. Behavior also sends information to physiological mechanisms, resulting in adjustment of birth and mortality rates. Behavior, thus, communicates the information necessary to increase the efficiency of use of energy. The next chapter will show how survival (which reflects efficiency) of a species may be affected by behavior.

References

Christian, J. J., and D. E. Davis. "Endocrines, Behavior, and Population," *Science, 146*:1550–1560 (1964).

Slobodkin, L. B. *Growth and Regulation of Animal Populations*. New York: Holt, Rinehart and Winston, 1961. viii + 184 pp.

Wynne-Edwards, V. C. *Animal Dispersion in Relation to Social Behaviour*. New York: Hafner Publishing Company, 1962. xi + 653 pp.

CHAPTER

7

Behavior and Survival of Populations

THE ROLE THAT BEHAVIOR may play in the survival of a total population rather than of a single individual has recently attracted attention. Since information on survival of populations is even more difficult to obtain than information on selective survival of individuals, and since the concept has only recently been formulated, few data can be cited. This chapter will therefore be somewhat speculative, pointing out current thought and indicating types of work that might be carried out in the future. Lack of data need not deter us from consideration of the concept as long as attempts to obtain and accumulate data continue. Let us remember that although Darwin emphasized the idea of survival of the fittest a century ago, data actually demonstrating survival of particular individuals in contrast to others have been hard to find. However, in recent years experiments on several species, butterflies in particular, have indicated that certain individuals are less apt to be taken by predators than are other individuals. The differential survival of individuals is relatively easy to visualize. Some particular animals are better able, through strength or alertness, to obtain food, resting places, and the other necessities for life. Furthermore, they succeed, in part through behavior and in part through some anatomical adaptation, in avoiding predators. These individuals thus will live longer and on the average will produce more progeny than will less adequately equipped individuals. In contrast, the survival of a total population is more difficult to comprehend. It is clear that a population consisting of identical individuals, each extremely well adapted to the environment, will survive far better than a population containing less well equipped individuals. This simple situation does not occur in populations because individual variation develops among the members of the population, making some animals better equipped than others. As this variation develops, individual survival will differ among the members of the population. Certain individuals will disappear and others will survive. Superimposed on individual variability is variation of the environment such that some features have survival value in certain conditions and other features in other conditions. Selection, of course, tends to promote the improvement of the particular populations. However, as the population increases and begins to impinge upon resources, pressures for survival increase. At this stage the organization of the population begins to select the individuals for survival. Disappearance or elimination of some individuals reduces somewhat the pressure on the resources, and thus the population as a whole is better able to maintain itself. This favorable feature is of such importance that mechanisms that eliminate individuals develop and persist, facilitating maintenance of the species. Indeed, the mortality of certain individuals is necessary for the survival of the species. Without the mortality of a few, the entire group would risk the danger of depleting the resources and dying out. Suppose we consider a very simple situation. Four roosters are kept in a pen where enough food is provided for two. The birds have the choice of dividing the food up equally or of giving the food to two individuals. In the first case, all would starve; in the second, two would survive at the expense of the other two. The latter choice is clearly to the benefit of the species, although the deprivation for the two that starve seems cruel.

Individual Survival

Before considering in some detail the problems of survival of populations, let us first examine, primarily for orientation and comparison, the survival of individuals within a population. It is, of course, true that individuals die as the result of external events such as starvation, weather, catastrophes, predators, and disease. At the moment, however, we are concerned only with the factors within a population acting to produce death and thus promoting survival of certain individuals in contrast to others. Animals may fight fiercely against individuals of their own species to settle questions of territory and rank (Chapter 5). Results of these encounters may be fatal for one or even both animals, but suitable behavioral devices usually prevent the encounter from reaching such a drastic stage. Behavioral adaptations have survival value, and deaths due to direct competition between individuals are relatively rare. It is advantageous for the species to resolve the problem of distribution of resources without a fatality for one of the individuals.

When an individual is defeated in an encounter, he leaves the area and attempts to find a different location. He may travel to unfamiliar habitats and sooner or later find a location that appears suitable. Naturally, his first problem is whether another individual of the same species already owns the land. This question may soon be answered in a manner that forces the animal to continue his travels. For example, in the early fall young woodchucks leave the burrow where they were raised and begin to wander. They may travel a considerable distance in search of suitable locations not already belonging to other woodchucks. During this time, as well as in the following spring, while the yearling animals are traveling about, the adults stay at the same burrow, and thus a youngster may have a hard time finding a location. Whether the social organization is territorial, social rank, or a combination of both, animals unable to compete will travel considerable distances before finding a new location. In some species (as mentioned in Chapter 6) movement or emigration of individuals is the major means of reducing population pressure and avoiding direct conflicts at high densities. In other species movement may be less important, though present, and a reduction of reproductive success may be the chief means of reducing the population pressure. Again, individuals that are unable to maintain a territory or are low in the social rank may become outcasts, completely unable to find a suitable place for reproduction. This phenomenon is perhaps best illustrated by the elaborate social organization of the Australian magpie. These birds live in groups varying from a few individuals to flocks of a hundred or more. The flocks may be classified in several types, beginning with the birds that have excellent habitat and reproduce as a group; other flocks live peripherally to these successful groups and may begin reproductive behavior but rarely succeed in producing young; finally, some individuals live in large nomadic groups and in some cases never succeed in producing young during their lifetime. These latter birds may be either outcasts or young that have not yet been able to establish a relationship with the successful flock. In this case, the inhibition of reproduction consists largely of exclusion from a suitable habitat and a breeding group. In other species, such as the domestic fowl, it is well known that within a group certain individuals may be psychologically unable to breed, simply existing as part of the group but adding nothing to its number of individuals.

The simple device of preventing normal growth is still another process for reducing individual survival. The stunting of fish has been noticed and amply documented for several decades. The situation is simply that individuals in dense populations do not grow adequately and hence produce only small numbers of progeny, if

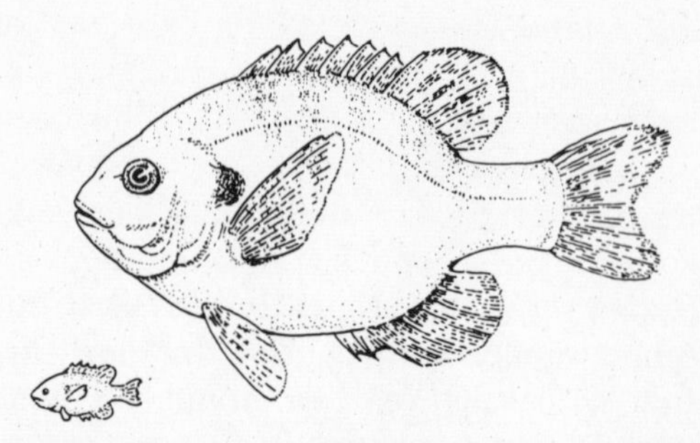

Figure 7·1. A comparison of growth of bluegills in one year. The small fish were in a population of 180,000 per acre, the large in 1,500 per acre. [From H. S. Swingle and E. V. Smith, in Agricultural Experiment Station Bulletin No. 254, 1947, published by Alabama Polytechnic Institute, Auburn University.]

any. This same procedure takes place to a limited extent in mammals and probably to a great extent in other vertebrates, although data are relatively scarce. The net result of this process again is the reduction in the number of individuals produced.

The preceding comments apply to survival of individuals, in part in the sense of the actual animal itself and in part in the survival of individuals that have a particular set of genes. From this description it is clear that a population has a number of processes that will, in one way or another, affect the survival of particular individuals.

Population Survival

We are now ready to consider the survival of a population as a whole and hence the survival of a species. It is, of course, apparent that a species contains somewhat discrete populations which may independently change in numbers. A few species, such as the Kirtland's warbler, consist of a few hundred individuals living in a relatively small habitat; the total species is essentially one population. However, most species have an extensive geographical distribution permitting division into separate segments. It is possible thus for one segment to increase or to decrease to extinction without altering the survival of the species as a whole. The decrease of a local population to zero is called local extinction. If this extinction is due to some temporary deficiency in the habitat, other individuals at some later time can come in and repopulate the area. In contrast, other populations may remain almost constant year after year rarely showing the phenomenon of local extinction. But it should be recognized that a species will eventually become extinct when local extinction happens simultaneously throughout the geographical distribution. Consider the records of field vole populations at five places in Holland. The increases differed but all reached low or zero levels simultaneously, resulting in extinction over a large area. Hence it can be said that eventual extinction of the species is absolutely certain.

While the preceding statements may seem somewhat fanciful, they are necessary for understanding the importance and nature of random fluctuations of populations. Animals living in habitats that change greatly from time to time will respond to these changes by increasing or decreasing in numbers. If the habitat is relatively stable or, as in the equatorial rain forests, has only one or two factors that change, the fluctuations will be relatively small and infrequent. However, many forms live in habitats such as deserts, temperate-zone forests, or the arctic, where changes may be rather frequent. In these habitats the species will increase or decrease in accordance with a particular situation. Since factors vary without synchrony, fluctuations in the population are random. It should be noted that randomness does not imply absence of cause (a fluctuation in a population must have a cause), but it does imply that so many causes act at so many different times that no regularity can be detected in the ups and downs. In some cases, however, one cause of change may be far more significant than all the others, producing population increases and decreases in a less random form, the changes occurring primarily with this particular cause. For example, mosquitoes primarily dependent upon rainfall are abundant in years of good rainfall and scarce in years of poor rainfall. These oscillations may assume some regularity if there are regular changes in the principal factor.

Populations with enormous fluctuations, such as the red algae of the Gulf of Mexico, are in danger of local and eventually total extinction, partly because they may exhaust the resources of their habitat. Species that develop mechanisms for slowing down the rate of increase or somehow preventing the population from attaining a very high level will, on the whole, reduce the frequency of local extinction and over the centuries reduce the likelihood of simultaneous local extinction over wide geographic areas. As an entity such species will tend to survive better than species that do not have a means for restricting excessive fluctuations. The situation is illustrated by the growth of populations resulting in what are called damped oscillations. This phenomenon can be graphed as a curve starting with a low number of animals, increasing to a relatively high number, and then declining or increasing in peaks and troughs of a constantly reduced amplitude until the population remains essentially stationary. Damping of oscillations occurs in populations

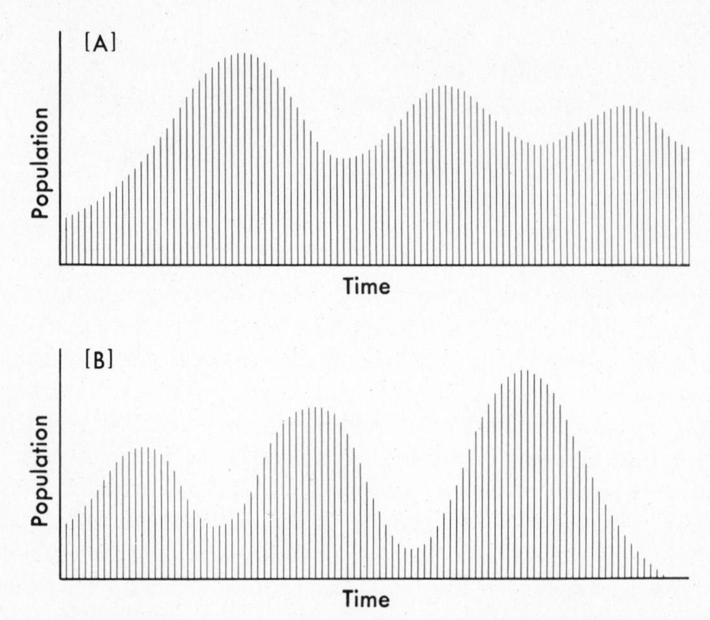

Figure 7·2. Contrast of damped oscillation and accentuated fluctuations. In **A** the population gradually adjusts to the environment and survives. In **B** the population, through positive feedback, increases its fluctuations, eventually becoming extinct—at least locally.

of higher animals, including insects and vertebrates, and decreases the likelihood of local extinction. The process occurs through negative feedback mechanisms.

In contrast, an increase in likelihood of extinction results from accentuated oscillations which may result from a positive feedback mechanism. The significance of such oscillations is that the catastrophe of local extinction will be reached much sooner. As time progresses, the population reaches higher peaks and lower troughs and very soon is in danger of local extinction. Examples of positive feedback in animals are not readily available; apparently it is too disastrous to survive. A hypothetical case for positive feedback can be postulated for an animal if large litters survive better than small litters, and hence a greater and greater increase in the reproductive rate occurs. Animals thus would increase at an increasing rate until the resources of the habitat were completely destroyed and the population inevitably crashed. This situation may occur in lemming or field vole populations, as indicated by the frequent fluctuations in their numbers, and there is a possibility also that it occurs in the populations of some deer, especially the mule deer. It is, of course, impossible to cite may cases of positive feedback in populations for the obvious reason that extinction is inevitable. All we have left are the species that have negative population feedback plus a few species that may have positive feedback and are getting out of control.

Mechanisms

Since it is clear that most species now existing have developed some sorts of mechanism for restricting fluctuations, it is important to consider the various types. First, we should mention various physiological mechanisms, since these presumably have replaced behavioral mechanisms in evolution. A mechanism that seems to be purely physiological is the production of toxic substances by many invertebrates and many vertebrates such as tadpoles and fish. This mechanism is not very satisfactory, in part because the toxic substances may persist a long time and in part because the quantities are inflexible on an individual basis. Thus, ten individuals produce ten times as much as one individual. Such a mechanism lacks the desirable qualities of density-dependence. Decreased metabolism is another physiological mechanism which results in lowered requirements for energy. This decrease seems to occur in some vertebrates during certain seasons and, of course, occurs among many invertebrates during times of inhospitable climatic conditions.

In contrast to physiological mechanisms, behavioral mechanisms have the advantage of being density-dependent. Stimulation of behavioral mechanisms comes from other individuals. An individual determines through his sense organs what conditions occur in the environment and then does something about them. It turns out that a principal component of the environment, at least for higher vertebrates and perhaps for insects, is other individuals of the same species. For example, a woodchuck spends most of his observing time looking for other woodchucks rather than looking for predators or other danger.

At the risk of apparently digressing it is desirable now to illustrate the basic concept of density-dependence. The essence of the idea is that the relative importance of some mortality factor increases as the density of the population increases. In the graph are indicated two situations. The lower dotted, horizontal line refers to mortality that is produced by factors whose effects are not related to density—

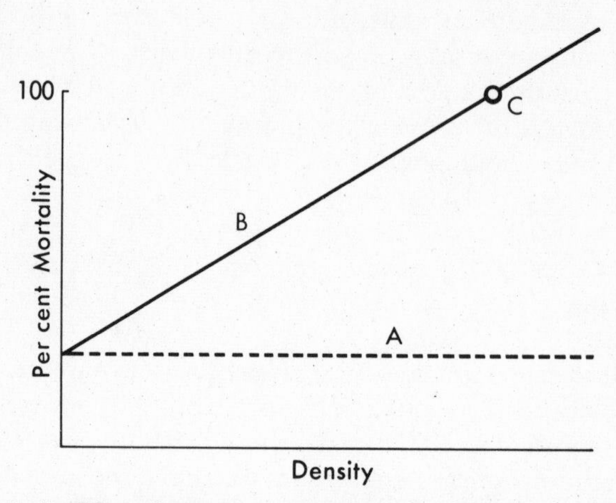

Figure 7·3. A simplified diagram of density dependence. Mortality refers to the percentage of new animals that die (not percentage of total); density should be measured in behavioral terms but usually means animals per acre. Some factors remove a constant percentage irrespective of density (*A*); others remove in accordance with density (*B*) until stability is reached (C) from either direction, because the number removed equals the number entering the population.

the so-called density-independent factors. In many situations climate or certain types of physiological disease cause mortality unrelated to the density of the individuals. The sloping line refers to that part of the total mortality produced by factors that act in an increasing proportion as the density of the population increases.

In a general way, predators are considered to be density-dependent, since at times of high numbers predators may find it easier to obtain their prey and thus act increasingly as the prey population increases. In fact, however, the action of predators is extremely erratic. In some cases the prey outstrips the predator so that actually a smaller and smaller proportion is taken, a process that is called inverse density-dependence. It is not appropriate here to discuss this concept in detail but an inescapable conclusion is that predators are not dependable as a means of holding down the population.

In contrast to the action of predators, the action of competition among individuals can result in density-dependent mortality. The competition is, of course, mediated through behavior of fighting and other activities. Theoretically, the number of interactions among individuals should follow the laws of random collisions and thus should be proportional to $(N^2 - N)/2$. Clearly, from this equation one can see that the number of collisions, which can be taken as a measure of competition, will increase roughly as a square of the number of individuals. Thus, the effects of competition should increase exponentially as the population increases. In the simplest version of this theory each collision or encounter between individuals could result in the death of other individuals. Under these circumstances, the effect would be strictly dependent on density and act in a very rigid manner. However, there have developed a variety of behavioral devices that mitigate the effects of a direct encounter. Returning to the information presented in Chapter 5, we remember that birds, for example, have developed a variety of behaviors, including bluffs and song, which mean that an encounter does not result in the death of one individual but simply in the exclusion of an individual from a particular place. Over a period of time, of course, an individual excluded from place after place will not reproduce and will die. This effect is not a direct one. Similarly the behavioral features of the social rank organization prevent each encounter from being fatal but permit the individual to survive, at least for a time, under circumstances that might eventually result in reproduction. It might be said that behavioral mechanisms soften the impact of competition and partially undo the effects of density-dependence.

Behavior thus becomes a means of population homeostasis, regulating the population toward an equilibrium with its environment. In this situation the population maintains close adjustment to the resources, and the boom and bust sequence of numbers rarely occurs. Also, a population is less likely to suffer local extinction and, of course, even less likely to suffer complete extinction as a result of chance synchrony of local extinction throughout a wide area. Clearly, a species that has behavioral mechanisms to prevent excessive increase and destruction of habitat will survive better than a species lacking these mechanisms. It is important to note that the behavioral mechanisms act throughout the fluctuations or oscillations that may occur in a population. Indeed, a population starting from a very small number of individuals in an uninhabited area will have some impact from the behavioral mechanisms at all stages of its increase. Obviously, the mechanisms are not noticeable or important in the early stages but only attain significance when the population begins to reach high levels.

The overwhelming importance of any population mechanism is its action as a negative feedback, holding down the rate of increase in numbers. However, various species have developed certain behavior patterns that act to reduce the effectiveness of the negative feedback. For example, the submission postures given by a defeated wolf prevent the victor, so to speak, from destroying the vanquished. While this behavioral device is unfortunate because it reduces the effectiveness of the negative feedback, it is perhaps balanced by the importance of permitting the defeated animal to escape, to leave the area, and perhaps to find an uninhabited or sparsely populated area where it can resettle. Thus, while at first sight behavioral mechanisms that reduce the effectiveness of negative feedback would appear to be disadvantageous to the species, apparently they are balanced over the centuries by the advantageous effect of emigration that permits survival in another place. However, a species that eliminates all of its negative feedbacks would soon eliminate, of course, the behavioral density-dependent features and would again be in the condition of a species without regulatory mechanisms on its increase. Under these circumstances, it would return to the very primitive systems which lack interindividual behaviors that can reflect population density.

Evolution of Behavioral Mechanisms. The level of attainment of behavioral mechanisms for negative feedback varies, of course, with the different groups of animals. It appears that primitive forms have rarely attained behavioral feedbacks; at least we have not recognized them. Thus, protozoa and many of the primitive metazoa are dependent usually on the environmental situation for the control of the population. Presumably these populations fluctuate up and down and only by chance survive as a species. There is, however, a recent report that parasitic trypanosomes produce substances that at high densities reduce growth of these protozoa. With the increase in anatomical complexity of animals, there arises the possibility of behavioral feedbacks; and, indeed, one might state that the effectiveness of behavioral feedbacks has been an important selective factor in the development of a complex anatomical organization. However, in the primitive phase of development of behavioral feedbacks different types of competition among individuals need to be considered.

The term scramble has been used by Nicholson to refer simply to unorganized competition of animals for some resource. It resembles a familiar children's game: someone throws a handful of peanuts into the air and allows the boys to fight for them. The scramble type of competition clearly occurs in a wide variety of species, principally primitive forms which include many of the insects. However, an organized type of competition can occur, dependent upon either a territory or a social organization. Suppose that the boys, instead of being equally free to catch peanuts, were lined up in rank so that the first individual was certain to get a peanut, and the second, and so on, for as long as the peanuts lasted. In this process certain individuals would be sure to get a part of the resources and certain individuals would be excluded. This type of organization conserves the energy of the top-ranking individuals thereby preventing the inefficient aspects of the scramble.

A behavioral device such as territory or social rank that conserves energy on this scale will, of course, have great survival value as a population phenomenon. Some of the invertebrates have a primitive type of territory, and at least certain individuals will remain for a long time in a small area. For example, limpets travel around on the ocean floor but generally remain within a small range. Certain insects, such as dragonflies, defend a territory at the edge of a stream or pond and so have first choice at the environmental requisites found in the area. Fish and amphibians have developed in many cases a very elaborate social rank or territory, fully obtaining the survival benefits from efficiency of utilization of the resources for the top-ranking or territorial individuals. Thus, behavior, by organizing a population, increases the efficiency of use of energy and mitigates the direct effects of competition.

The physiological mechanisms that administer the negative feedback are poorly known among most species. Among invertebrates and lower vertebrates little has been done to determine what particular organs and systems are involved. Little is known even in birds about the physiological feedbacks in wild populations. Among mammals considerable variation occurs from group to group and even among the different species. Thus far a few rodents, especially the house mouse, have been studied intensively (see Chapter 6) and provided most of the actual evidence for the theory. Even here there is some question as to how often these physiological feedbacks may attain importance in nature. Some work has been done on voles and their allies that suggests that while the behavioral feedback mechanism is present, it is far less well synchronized with population level than is the case in house mice. One might expect the mechanism to be more significant in herbivorous animals, which regularly risk the possibility of literally destroying their food supply. A little work done on some of the deer tribes suggests that, at least to a limited extent, feedbacks affect mortality and birth rates. While carnivores have not yet been studied, and perhaps because of their general scarcity will not be studied for some time to come, it may be that they never attain a density that would require a behavioral feedback mechanism.

Survival Value for the Species. The clear effect of the behavioral mechanisms acting through physiological negative feedback processes is to maximize efficiency of use of energy and to increase the proportion of total protoplasm contained within the fortunate species. Negative feedback behavior within individual populations, of course, prevents overexploitation of habitat and a decline in numbers. Furthermore, these processes prevent wastage of young and increase the efficiency of utilization of the resources. At highest efficiency every unit of energy eventually becomes part of a breeding adult. To attain this efficiency a number of behavioral requirements are involved. First, the species must obtain information concerning the resources in the environment. However, animals have not developed an ability to measure quantities of the environmental necessities; they simply use what they find to fill their daily needs and leave the rest. Nevertheless, they can measure, in a sense, the presence of individuals belonging to the same or other competing species and thereby get a rough measure of the quantities of requisites available in the environment. So, information about the presence of other members of the same species is as important as information about the actual quantities. The second requirement to attain efficiency is an organization which, of course, is developed and maintained through behavior. Animals have produced two types of social organization—territory and social rank—which probably are basically similar but simply show differences at the extremes. Without some organization, efficiency of utilization of resources is low. Last, animals need to develop connections between behavior and physiological mechanisms that can be used for feedback. The connections are organized along two lines, which again probably are not very different except in their anatomical arrangements. The brain and nervous system, which very rapidly conduct impulses, provide an immediate means for action after perception, through the sense organs, of some environmental feature. Also, various glands, through their hormones, provide a slow, chronic means of responding to the environment. Both the fast and the slow physiological mechanisms have a very important role to play. Consider a rooster in a pen. When a strange bird approaches, the rooster, through its sensory and nervous system, immediately becomes aware of the individual and moves to carry out appropriate actions. This rapid response takes care of the situation. However, in addition, the impulses go down through the brain to the adrenal system, where certain slow effects, as described in Chapter 5, occur. The result eventually is a reduction in the reproductive rate and an increase in the mortality rate. It clearly is to the advantage of a species to have anatomical adjustments that can take care of an immediate situation and others that can average the circumstances over a period of time.

As indicated in the first part of the chapter, much of the discussion has been speculative, since at this stage we lack adequate experimental information. It seems worthwhile, however, in the next chapter to consider how available facts and the current ideas may apply to humans.

CHAPTER

8

Behavior of Man

MAN HAS RECEIVED AN anatomical and physiological legacy from other vertebrates. His behavioral equipment of sense organs, nerves, and hormones is basically the same as that of other mammals and in many ways very similar to that of other vertebrates. A detailed description of these structures and their physiology can be found in numerous textbooks. The important point in the present discussion is to consider the organization of behavior of man and the new developments produced by man.

Man's responses to environmental stimuli are essentially the same as those of other vertebrates in anatomical, physiological, and behavioral characteristics. When a man is cold, he attempts to get into a warmer place. When something tastes good, man responds appropriately. In addition, his social organization is derived directly from that of primates and parallels the organization of a large number of vertebrates. Each tribe in primitive man was organized to defend a territory. For example, data are available for aborigines in Australia, where Birdsell found that a tribe of approximately 500 persons defended a large tract of land. The size of the tract was closely related to the resources, and a very good correlation inversely related the quantity of resources to the size of the tract. The number 500 seemed to be in some way an optimum, since the number in several tribes varied only slightly from this total. Presumably, a smaller size was not adequate for defense and survival, and a larger size resulted in a splitting off or budding of part of the group. Within the tribe was established a social rank consisting of chiefs and a series of subordinates. This organization is, of course, parallel to that found in numbers of primates including macaques and the gorilla.

New Developments

Based on the equipment and organization of vertebrates, man has developed new features that have made him the most abundant mammal in the world. Technology has resulted in the production of substitutes for sense organs which can receive kinds of stimuli other animals cannot use. Consider a simple example of the radio and television. Here man has invented a mechanical device that can respond to waves from the environment. This device changes the waves into stimuli that can be received by the ears and eyes. At the moment, there seems to be no limit to the number of external stimuli that can be harnessed by man's technology and put to use to inform him about environmental conditions and to improve his ability to communicate. In addition, technology has developed a number of means for man to do something about his environmental conditions. A very simple example is the heating and cooling now widely used throughout the world. Man has developed machines to reduce the variability of the environmental temperature and thus permit him to live in a uniform environment. These devices should be considered as additional homeostatic mechanisms, completely analogous to the physiological mechanisms for heating and cooling. Technological devices reduce the burden on the physiological and behavioral mechanisms and greatly increase the efficiency of use of energy by man himself.

Another development has been the elaborate increase in nongenetic transmission of information. Animals in general can give to the next generation information in two categories. The first is genetic, which consists of innate responses to environmental cues. For example, a very young lamprey, before it has been exposed to any other fish, will respond to the chemicals produced by trout by swimming in their direction. The lamprey has a genetically based response to specific amines. In addition to such genetic transmission of responses to information are the nongenetic or learned features. Animals at all stages of evolutionary complexity learn to respond to particular stimuli. Even the one-celled forms may show some sort of change of behavior after experience with adverse stimuli. The learning ability of insects and vertebrates is enormous. In part learning depends on direct experience, favorable or unfavorable, with the object; and in part it depends upon demonstration by other animals or imitation of other animals. Generally speaking, there is a trend toward efficiency in the direction of genetic transmission, since, under these circumstances, it is not necessary for each animal to learn by actual experience that an object is desirable or undesirable. Vertebrates have developed, to a considerable degree, the ability to transfer information from one generation to another by example. However, as every college student will admit, such learning requires effort. Man has developed the process of writing, which is a means for transfer of information. Thus, information can be stored in books or other devices and used by any individual who has the ability and patience to dig it out. At the present time, the quantity of information stored has become so immense that a large amount of energy is being spent in devising means for finding and making available what information is needed.

In man restrictions have developed on the consequences of decisions that would result in poor survival. Among animals a decision that may result in death is rarely modified or prevented by other individuals. Man, however, has developed the virtues of charity, which really means that a person who makes the wrong decision need not necessarily suffer its consequences. So, the survival of individuals is not necessarily connected to their everyday behavior but may be altered by the behavior of other individuals.

Another new development by man is the elaborate set of rules, either written or unwritten, concerning his behavior. These rules govern his daily life in his relations with other individuals and are called by names such as manners, ethics, or custom. In addition, there are elaborate sets of rules for governing the behavior of groups of men in the world. These range from decisions by the World Court at The Hague to the charter of the United Nations.

Survival

The survival of individuals has reached a very high level in man. While it is true that all persons eventually die, nevertheless the survival rate of adults has become so high that we simply assume a person will live until he is 70 or 80 years old. Furthermore, the mortality of infants has decreased to a very low level. This high survival comes about through behaviors that maintain existence under very well controlled and safe circumstances. The reproductive rate of man has declined to a low level, but survival is so high that there is now a frightening increase in the number of individuals. Man must consider whether the rates of increase are adequately under control for the survival of the species. It was pointed out in the preceding chapter that animals that do not have adequate control of their population develop a sequence of increases and decreases that, if maintained, will soon lead to extinction. Man needs to ask whether he has sufficient negative feedbacks on the population growth to prevent this boom and bust sequence of population numbers. Let us review (from Chapter 7) the general factors controlling populations.

Habitat conditions (except certain extremes) do not limit human populations. Predators and disease no longer kill large numbers and thus cannot control the population. Other individuals or groups, thanks to rules among nations, no longer can regularly restrict by war the number of men. What now can prevent man from increasing, as do the lemmings, until his population occupies and destroys his habitat? Man must develop negative feedbacks to hold down the increase to a level compatible with the increase in capacity of the universe to contain man. These feedbacks must be economic rewards for a low reproductive rate. For example, the present income tax deduction for children is a positive feedback, encouraging reproduction. It should be replaced by a graduated penalty for larger numbers of children, thereby acting as a negative feedback. An unfavorable reception for this suggestion is a measure of the difficulty that man will have in developing negative feedbacks. The same problems arise in other situations such as unemployment.

Let us, however, be optimistic and assume that man does develop negative feedbacks to control his population. Will evolution stop? Will man develop such a steady state that through behavior every response is accurately and promptly adjusted to the environment? Under these circumstances the rules of behavior will be so rigidly observed that little or no variation is possible, and man and his completely domesticated world will reach a steady state of existence.

From a behavior viewpoint man has an interesting prospect for the future. As indicated, man is now approaching domination of all living things by his ability to manage his environment. In contrast to most animals, man, in common with some mammals, has developed a new mechanism for transmission of information to the next generation. Through language, information about actions can spread throughout the world and, thanks to communications, be known in a matter of minutes to anyone who cares. Thus, integration of the world is approaching a point at which the human population will be one unit. As a consequence of this integration, the population is increasing at a rate unequaled in history.

This increase in numbers and in technological devices cannot continue indefinitely. Consider the changes in numbers of humans. At present there are 3 billion, expected to double in about 40 years. In the year 2000 there could be 6 billion; in 2040, 12 billion, and so on. Such numbers cannot be supported even on a low level of subsistence. Thus, the human population must level off at some number dictated by a plateau in technological devices that integrate our behavior through communication.

Plateaus in technological equipment seem to be approaching. For example, many feel that nothing is to be gained by having a bigger bomb—we can already destroy the world. Little is to be gained by more rapid computers—most calculations require only a few seconds. We are reaching the limit in many things. Note that machines have replaced muscle in the production of work and even more importantly have replaced nerves and hormones in communication. Through the development of nonliving tools, man will integrate his behavior throughout the world and can stabilize human populations by the prompt application of negative feedbacks.

The speed of communication is important in understanding fluctuations. When a lag occurs in a negative feedback, there is, of course, time for the system to deviate from the point of stability and so require greater action by the feedback. In contrast, when little or no lag occurs, the system deviates only slightly before it is corrected. Thus, speedy communications will enhance stability. The prospect of a completely stable world is in sight. What might it be like?

Behavior throughout the world will be ritualized and uniform. Clothes, table manners, and other activities will show little variation. Language (perhaps completely symbolic) will be universal with a few pockets of dialects remaining. Education to a high level and age will be universal. Careers will be dictated by exhaustive tests of abilities (which will be quite uniform) and by needs of the system. Only a little energy will be spent in producing materials; most energy will be used in services. Innovations will be rare. The population will have very few young people. The old folks will have ample recreational means to fill their time. Life will be placid and uneventful. Behavior through its integrating power will produce security for all in the world.

Index